BLUEPRINTS

Reading Activities Resource Bank

Carol Cort

Stanley Thornes (Publishers) Ltd

Do you receive *BLUEPRINTS NEWS*?

Blueprints is an expanding series of practical teacher's ideas books and photocopiable resources for use in primary schools. Books are available for separate infant and junior age ranges for every core and foundation subject, as well as for an ever widening range of other primary teaching needs. These include **Blueprints Primary English** books and **Blueprints Resource Banks**. **Blueprints** are carefully structured around the demands of the National Curriculum in England and Wales, but are used successfully by schools and teachers in Scotland, Northern Ireland and elsewhere.

Blueprints provide:

- *Total curriculum coverage*
- *Hundreds of practical ideas*
- *Books specifically for the age range you teach*
- *Flexible resources for the whole school or for individual teachers*
- *Excellent photocopiable sheets – ideal for assessment and children's work profiles*
- *Supreme value.*

Books may be bought by credit card over the telephone and information obtained on **(01242) 577944**. Alternatively, photocopy and return this **FREEPOST** form to receive **Blueprints News**, our regular update on all new and existing titles. You may also like to add the name of a friend who would be interested in being on the mailing list.

Please add my name to the **BLUEPRINTS NEWS** mailing list.

Mr/Mrs/Miss/Ms _____

Home address _____

_____ Postcode _____

School address _____

_____ Postcode _____

Please also send **BLUEPRINTS NEWS** to:

Mr/Mrs/Miss/Ms _____

Address _____

_____ Postcode _____

To: Marketing Services Dept., Stanley Thornes Ltd, FREEPOST (GR 782), Cheltenham, GL50 1BR

Acknowledgements

The publishers acknowledge that this book is structured around the readability levels set out in *Individualised Reading – a teacher guide to readability levels at Key Stages 1 and 2* compiled by Cliff Moon and published annually by The Reading and Language Information Centre, University of Reading, Bulmershe Court, Early, Reading RG6 1HY

Text © Carol Cort 1994
Original line illustrations by Barry Jackson © Stanley Thornes (Publishers) Ltd 1994

The right of Carol Cort to be identified as author of this work has been asserted by her in accordance with the Copyright, Designs and Patents Act 1988.

First published in 1994 by
Stanley Thornes (Publishers) Ltd
Ellenborough House
Wellington Street
CHELTENHAM GL50 1YW
England

Reprinted 1994, 1995

Typeset by Tech-Set, Gateshead, Tyne & Wear.
Printed and bound in Great Britain.

A catalogue record for this book is available from the British Library.

ISBN 0–7487–1730–7

CONTENTS

Introduction   1
Reading Scheme index   2
Making and using the activities   3
The Copymasters 1–147

General Level
  1 Match the letters
  2 The Alphabet 1
  3 The Alphabet 2
  4 Build Soldier Sam 1
  5 Build Soldier Sam 2
  6 Build the train

Yellow Level
  7 Find the pair

White Level
  8 Dominoes
  9 Jigsaws
 10 Find the pair
 11 Dominoes
 12 Jigsaws
 13 Find the pair 1
 14 Find the pair 2
 15 Dominoes
 16 Jigsaws

Dark blue Level
 17 Find the pair
 18 Dominoes
 19 Jigsaws
 20 Find the pair
 21 Match the words

General Level
 22 Build Teddy 1
 23 Build Teddy 2
 24 The teddy track game 1
 25 The teddy track game 2
 26 Pick the coloured apples game 1
 27 Pick the coloured apples game 2

Pink Level
 28 Around the school dominoes
 29 Match the words
 30 Dominoes
 31 Find the pair 1
 32 Find the pair 2
 33 Dominoes
 34 Jigsaws
 35 Dominoes
 36 Jigsaws
 37 Dominoes

 38 Dominoes
 39 Find the pair 1
 40 Find the pair 2
 41 Pirate dominoes

General Level
 42 Colour snap 1
 43 Colour snap 2
 44 Word Ahoy match the words 1
 45 Word Ahoy match the words 2
 46 Match the words vocabulary list 1
 47 Match the words vocabulary list 2
 48 Match the words vocabulary list 3
 49 Word Ahoy worksheet
 50 Build Father Christmas 1
 51 Build Father Christmas 2
 52 Match the words
 53 Find the pair opposites 1
 54 Find the pair opposites 2
 55 Find the pair opposites 3
 56 Find the pair opposites 4

Brown Level
 57 Match the words
 58 Match the words
 59 Dominoes
 60 Dominoes
 61 Jigsaws
 62 Dominoes
 63 Find the pair 1
 64 Find the pair 2
 65 Jigsaws
 66 Dominoes
 67 Find the pair 1
 68 Find the pair 2
 69 Jigsaws
 70 Match the words
 71 Dominoes
 72 Jigsaws
 73 Find the pair 1
 74 Find the pair 2
 75 Dominoes
 76 Jigsaws
 77 Dominoes
 78 Dominoes
 79 Find the pair 1
 80 Find the pair 2
 81 Dominoes
 82 Jigsaws
 83 Find the pair 1
 84 Find the pair 2
 85 Dominoes
 86 Jigsaws

87 Dominoes
88 Dominoes
89 Find the pair 1
90 Find the pair 2
91 Pirate dominoes
92 Build Pirate Pete 1
93 Build Pirate Pete 2
94 Pirate Island track game 1
95 Pirate Island track game 2
96 Pirate find the pair 1
97 Pirate find the pair 2
98 Dominoes
99 Pirate find the pair 1
100 Pirate find the pair 2
101 Pirate Pete match the words

General Level
102 Build the racing car 1
103 Build the racing car 2
104 The race track game 1
105 The race track game 2

Green Level
106 Dominoes
107 Find the pair 1
108 Find the pair 2
109 Dominoes
110 Jigsaws
111 Find the pair 1
112 Find the pair 2
113 Dominoes
114 Jigsaws
115 Find the pair 1
116 Find the pair 2

117 Match the words
118 Dominoes
119 Around the park dominoes
120 Around the town dominoes
121 Around the town dominoes
122 Dominoes
123 Jigsaws
124 Dominoes
125 Find the pair 1
126 Find the pair 2
127 Dominoes
128 Jigsaws
129 Find the pair 1
130 Find the pair 2
131 Dominoes
132 Jigsaws
133 Dominoes
134 Jigsaws
135 Dominoes
136 Jigsaws
137 Dominoes
138 Dominoes
139 Find the pair 1
140 Find the pair 2
141 Dominoes

General Level
142 Build Wordal 1
143 Build Wordal 2
144 Build Asta the Alien 1
145 Build Asta the Alien 2
146 The planet race track game 1
147 The planet race track game 2

INTRODUCTION

The *Reading Activities Resource Bank* is a comprehensive compendium of 147 photocopiable pages of activities and games for use alongside most commonly used reading schemes and the colour coding of *Individualised Reading* (published by the Reading and Language Information Centre, University of Reading). It aims to develop essential sight-reading vocabulary skills, improve memory span and build self-confidence.

Most primary schools will have banks of reading activities, either bought or home-made, to support their reading programmes. This book provides a huge bank of such materials ready-made for use in the classroom that will save you both time and money. It allows you to make up carefully graded, relevant activities and games at a fraction of the cost of commercially bought ones. It also means that a lost piece does not cause problems; you simply photocopy the sheet again to replace it.

The activities are highly versatile. They can be photocopied directly onto card or photocopied onto paper and stuck onto card. The materials may then be coloured and covered for permanent use, or quickly run off on paper for more immediate classroom use. You will find practical instructions in the section on 'Making and using the activities'. Manufacture of the games is an ideal activity for parent helpers either at home or at school. As the costs of producing activities are minimal you can even send sheets of games home to be made up and practised with parents.

The *Reading Activities Resource Bank* covers the common early sight vocabulary which you can expect to find in most infant reading schemes. It is particularly compatible with the following reading schemes and you will find a chart on page vi explaining the coverage:

- 1, 2, 3 and Away
- Ginn 360
- Ginn Upstarts
- Oxford Reading Tree
- Griffin Pirate Stories
- Story Chest

Even if you are not specifically using one of these schemes you will find that the games will cover the basic sight vocabulary your children use. The games are structured around the colour coded levels of *Individualised Reading*, the regular publication from the Reading and Language Information Centre at Reading University. You will find their address within the Acknowledgements at the front of this book. Thus the coloured levels in this book refer to the colour coding of *Individualised Reading*. Interspersed between these colour coded activities you will find activities referred to as 'General Level'. Most of these are project based and are positioned within the book at stages where such projects would seem appropriate. However, due to their flexibility, the General activities can be adapted and used at any stage to enhance class projects and stimulate interest.

The games are of many different types. They include:

- Find the pair games
- Self-check matching jigsaws
- Touch cards
- Building activities
- Dominoes
- Jigsaws
- Word-matching games
- Snap games
- Track board games

Most of the games can be used flexibly with either individuals or with groups and many have a self-correcting element so that they can be played without adult supervision. You will find general instructions for playing the games on pages 3–8.

All the games have been extensively trialled and played with real children in real classrooms. They are stimulating, fun to play – and they work. Once you have started to work with the activities we think you will find this book an absolutely invaluable resource to return to again and again.

READING SCHEME INDEX

The index below indicates where you will find coverage of the vocabulary compatible with particular reading schemes at successive levels of difficulty. As most schemes share core vocabulary, the activities are usually devised for common use across schemes.

1, 2, 3 and Away

1, 2, 3, 4, 5, 6, 7, 8, 9, 10, 11, 12, 17, 18, 19, 20, 21, 22, 23, 24, 25, 26, 27, 28, 29, 30, 42, 43, 44, 45, 46, 47, 48, 49, 50, 51, 52, 53, 54, 55, 56, 57, 58, 63, 64, 65, 66, 67, 68, 69, 70, 71, 72, 73, 102, 103, 104, 105, 113, 114, 115, 116, 117, 119, 120, 121, 139, 140, 142, 143, 144, 145, 146 and 147.

Ginn 360

1, 2, 3, 4, 5, 6, 13, 14, 15, 16, 21, 22, 23, 24, 25, 26, 27, 28, 29, 38, 39, 40, 41, 42, 43, 44, 45, 46, 47, 48, 49, 50, 51, 52, 53, 54, 55, 56, 57, 58, 59, 70, 75, 76, 102, 103, 104, 105, 110, 117, 119, 120, 121, 131, 142, 143, 144, 145, 146 and 147.

Ginn Upstarts

1, 2, 3, 4, 5, 6, 21, 22, 23, 24, 25, 26, 27, 28, 29, 31, 32, 34, 35, 36, 37, 42, 43, 44, 45, 46, 47, 48, 49, 50, 51, 52, 53, 54, 55, 56, 57, 58, 59, 60, 61, 62, 63, 75, 86, 87, 88, 89, 90, 92, 93, 94, 95, 102, 103, 104, 105, 106, 107, 108, 109, 110, 111, 112, 117, 118, 119, 120, 121, 131, 132, 133, 142, 143, 144, 145, 146 and 147.

Oxford Reading Tree

1, 2, 3, 4, 5, 6, 9, 12, 21, 22, 23, 24, 25, 26, 27, 28, 29, 42, 43, 45, 46, 47, 48, 49, 50, 51, 52, 53, 54, 55, 56, 57, 58, 59, 70, 76, 77, 78, 79, 80, 81, 82, 83, 84, 85. 86, 87, 88, 89, 90, 91, 92, 93, 94, 95, 102, 103, 104, 117, 119, 120, 121, 122, 123, 124, 125, 126, 127, 128, 129, 130, 134, 136, 137, 138, 142, 143, 144, 145, 146 and 147.

Griffin Pirate Stories

1, 2, 3, 4, 5, 6, 21, 22, 23, 24, 25, 26, 27, 28, 29, 42, 43, 44, 45, 46, 47, 48, 49, 50, 51, 52, 53, 54, 55, 56, 57, 58, 70, 91, 92, 93, 94, 95, 96, 97, 98, 99, 100, 101, 102, 103, 104, 105, 117, 119, 120, 121, 142, 143, 144, 145, 146 and 147.

Story Chest

Due to the nature of these books the vocabulary is spread throughout the book. Copymasters of use include:

1, 2, 3, 4, 5, 6, 16, 17, 21, 22, 23, 24, 25, 26, 27, 28, 29, 39, 40, 42, 43, 44, 45, 46, 47, 48, 49, 50, 51, 52, 53, 54, 55, 56, 57, 58, 63, 64, 65, 70, 82, 92, 93, 94, 95, 98, 101, 102, 103, 104, 105, 117, 142, 143, 144, 145, 146 and 147.

MAKING AND USING THE ACTIVITIES

GENERAL INSTRUCTIONS

The activities in this book can be prepared in three different ways.

a) Photocopied directly on to card.
b) Photocopied onto paper.
c) As in b) and glued onto card.

Preparation

1 Photocopy the copymasters as required.
2 Colour the copies and then, if required, stick the paper onto card.
3 Cut out all the pieces.
4 Run a wide felt-tipped pen around the edge of the cards to obtain a professional-looking finish.

If the pen is used half on the card as shown no ruler is necessary. This technique may require practice but it is worth while as considerable time can be saved. Each complete set should be edged with the same colour pen so that pieces can be returned to their correct places easily.

5 Cover all pieces, on both sides, with transparent adhesive plastic, e.g. Coverlon®.

Several cards can be covered at the same time.

6 Cut around the covered pieces leaving a small border. The cutting action seals the plastic sheets together. The activity is now ready for use.

MAKING AND PLAYING THE GAMES

There are several main types of games in this book which provide reading practice at successive levels. The main types of games are outlined in this section.

Find the pair

Copymasters 7, 10, 13–14, 17, 20, 31–2, 39–40, 53–6, 63–4, 67–8, 73–4, 79–80, 83–4, 89–90, 96–7, 99, 100, 107–8, 111–12, 115–16, 125–6, 129–30 and 139–40.
An activity for two or three children

Objective of the activity
To improve the child's memory span whilst reinforcing reading vocabulary in a meaningful way.

Preparation
Each set of picture cards is immediately followed by the corresponding vocabulary set, both must be photocopied.

a) Photocopy the required sheets.
b) Colour and cut out as explained in the General instructions on page 3. At this point the cards should be marked with matching strips so that one set can be used for several activities, see copymaster 7. Each pair must have a unique pair of marks. By changing the position, colour and shape of the marks many sets can be used together.
c) Complete the preparation as in the General instructions.

To use the activity
1   The cards are mixed up and placed face down on a table in rows to form a rectangle.
2   Each child in turn may turn over any two cards and he or she must allow all the children to have a good view. If the cards do not match he or she must replace them, face down, in their original places.
3   If the cards selected are a pair, word matching picture, he or she keeps them and takes another turn. The child may do this until he or she fails to find a pair.
4   The game continues until all the pairs have been found. The winner is the child with the most pairs. More sets of 'Find the pair' cards can easily be produced using the domino copies, which could be enlarged by means of a photocopier.

Self-check matching jigsaws
Objective of the activity
To build self-confidence by providing a self-correcting method of learning vocabulary.

Preparation
Prepare as for 'Find the pair' cards.
The number of jigsaws given to a child should depend on the ability of the child. A set may be built up slowly or lengthened by joining two sets. Problem words can easily be carried forward and added to the next vocabulary.

To use the activity
1   The cards are mixed up and then spread out face up.
2   The child looks at the pictures and tries to find the corresponding card by reading the words. The matching marks are there to help.
3   When all the cards are paired the child should be asked to read the words.

Once a child is familiar with the vocabulary on the cards the set cards can be used to play a game. For example, 'Find the pair' or 'Match the jigsaw'.

Match the jigsaw
An activity for two children.

Object of the activity
To revise the vocabulary used in the Self-check game.

To use the activity
1   The cards are mixed up and half are placed face up on a table.
2   The second half are placed in a pile face up.
3   The first child takes the top card off the pile and he or she tries to match it with the cards already displayed. If it matches he or she takes the pair. If not the card is placed with those on the table.
4   The second child now tries to match a card in the same way.
5   When all the cards in the pile have been used the game continues with the children collecting the pairs from the table. The winner is the child with the most cards.

Touch cards
Objective of the activity
To build self-confidence by presenting reading vocabulary in a meaningful and self-correcting way.

Preparation
These cards are produced using the 'Find the pair' copymasters.
a) Photocopy the required copymasters of 'Find the pair' cards, colour and cut out as in the General instructions on page 3.
b) Glue each vocabulary card back to back with its corresponding picture card. Then cover as usual.
    There are many ways to use these cards.

Activity 1
For one child
1   The touch cards are laid out with the words facing up.
2   The child points to a card, reads the word and then checks the picture to see if he or she is correct. If correct the child collects the card, if not it remains on the table and another card is chosen. The activity is continued until all the cards have been collected.

Activity 2
For one child
The same process is followed but this time the child reads the words to an adult. This helps to build confidence.

Activity 3
For two children
The cards are laid out with the words facing up. The children take turns to read a word of their choice, using the pictures to check they are correct. Each child collects correctly read cards and the child with the most cards is the winner.

Activity 4
For two children
1   The cards are placed in a pile, words facing upwards and the children take turns to read the top card.
2   If the card is read correctly it is collected, if not it is placed in a new pile picture upwards, next to the original stack.
3   When the reading pile is completed the wrongly-read cards are turned over and the procedure is repeated until all the cards have been correctly read.

Building activities
This series of building activities includes: Soldier Sam (copymasters 4–5), the train (copymaster 6), Teddy (copymasters 22–3), Father Christmas (copymasters 50–1), Pirate Pete (copymasters 92–3), the racing car (copymasters 102–3), Wordal (copymasters 142–3) and Astra the Alien (copymasters 144–5).

Objective of the activity
The aim of the activity is to build a child's self-confidence.
    It is a game for 2–6 children. Each child needs a set of equipment. The set consists of two prepared photo-copied copymasters together with suitable vocabulary cards produced from the 'Find the pair' cards.

Preparation
a) Photocopy the required number of sets.
b) Colour the copies.
c) Cut the second copymaster into its component parts as shown on the base board copymaster. Each part is numbered from 1 to 6.
d) To make the game easy to use; stick small pieces of *Velcro*® on the back of the six pieces and on the corresponding places on the base board.
e) Cover all the pieces including the base board.

To use the activity
1   Each child sets up his or her equipment as shown on the following page.
2   The children throw the die in turn and the child with the highest score begins and play continues in a clockwise direction.
3   The first child reads their top vocabulary card. If it is read correctly they throw the die and collect the corresponding piece to place on their board.
4   The other children take their turns in the same way.
5   If the child already has the number shown on the die he or she collects a counter. Three counters may be exchanged for any piece the child chooses. The first child to fill their board is the winner.

Dominoes
Copymasters 8, 11, 15, 18, 28, 30, 33, 35, 37, 38, 41, 59–60, 62, 66, 71, 75, 77–8, 81, 85, 87–8, 91, 98, 106, 109, 113, 118–22, 124, 127, 131, 133, 135, 137–8 and 141.

Reading cards

Objective of the activity
To provide a reading vocabulary in a meaningful repetitive way.

Preparation
a) Photocopy the required copymaster.
b) Make up the cards as directed in the General instructions. When preparing the dominoes cut along the dotted lines.
c) Choose a starting card and mark it on the back prior to covering.

To use the activity
1 The cards are divided equally between two children.
2 The child with the starting card places it face up on the table.
3 The second child looks at his or her cards to try to find a match, word to picture or picture to word. If he or she has a suitable card it is placed to match.
4 The first child continues in the same way.
5 If a child does not have a matching card he or she misses his or her turn.
   The winner is the first child to have no cards left.

Jigsaws
Copymasters 9, 12, 16, 19, 34, 36, 61, 65, 69, 72, 76, 82, 86, 110, 114, 123, 128, 132, 134 and 136.

Objective of the activity
The aim of this activity is to provide a self-correcting and therefore confidence-building method of presenting vocabulary in a meaningful and repetitive way.

Preparation
a) Photocopy the required copymaster and prepare as in the General instructions.
b) Cut each of the nine small jigsaws into two as shown.

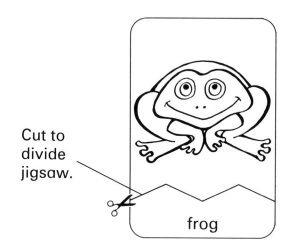

Cut to divide jigsaw.

frog

To use the activity
The child should be given a suitable number of the small jigsaws to sort. The number given should depend on the child's ability. Sets can be built up slowly, added to and repeated.

Soldier Sam Alphabet strips
Copymasters 2–3.

Objective of the activity
To provide an interesting way to revise alphabetical order.

Preparation
a) Photocopy copymasters 2 and 3.
b) Colour the copy of copymaster 2.
c) Cut out the two slots as marked on Sam and cut out the alphabet strips on copymaster 3.
d) Cover the pieces in transparent adhesive plastic.
e) Cut a single slit in the plastic over each slot.

To use the activity
1 Slide an alphabet strip through the cut slots from behind. Alphabet strips have been provided in both right-handed and left-handed form.

2   Sam can now be used to help the children keep their place when writing the alphabet or to find the letter that comes before or after a given letter.

Match the letters/words
Copymasters 1, 21, 52, 57–8, 70, 101 and 117.

Objective of the activity
'Match the letters' (copymaster 1) can be used to reinforce alphabetical order. 'Match the words' copymasters are intended to present words that cannot be represented graphically.

Preparation
These sets consist of a base board and individual tiles. Photocopy and prepare the sets as in the General instructions.

To use the activity
1   Each child requires a set consisting of a base board and word tiles.
2   The children are asked to match the tiles to the words on the base board.
3   This may be a timed activity or the children may take turns to read a word aloud as they each fill in their own base board. A wrongly-read word cannot be collected and the first child to fill their board is the winner.

This is an ideal game for the children to take home to practise. The worksheet on copymaster 49 may be used to extend these activities. You will need to photocopy Copymaster 101 twice. Use one copy as the baseboard and use the other copy to make the tiles.

Word Ahoy
Copymasters 44–9

Objective of the activity
This is a large word-matching activity intended to give the teacher a wide choice of vocabulary, to suit an individual child or class.

Preparation
a) Photocopy copymasters 44 and 45 once and copymasters 46, 47 and 48 twice.
b) Colour the copies of copymasters 44 and 45. Trim their edges and join them together using adhesive tape to form a base board.
c) Cut out the vocabulary tiles on copymasters 47, 48 and 49.
d) Cover the board and the vocabulary tiles in transparent adhesive plastic.

To use the activity
1   From the vocabulary copymasters the teacher takes two copies of the words of her choice. One copy is then stuck onto the base board in the spaces on the ship, using double sided tape or *Velcro*®.
2   The child is given the prepared base board together with the other set of word tiles and asked to match the words.

The worksheet printed on copymaster 49 may be used to extend this activity.

Pick the coloured apples
Copymasters 26–7

Objective of the game
To present reading vocabulary in a meaningful and repetitive way.
   An activity for two children.

Equipment needed
A coloured die showing the six colours named on the boards. This can easily be made using a wooden cube and sticky paper.

Preparation
a) Photocopy copymasters 26 and 27 as in the General instructions.
b) Colour the sheets taking care to colour four of the circles in each of the given colours.
c) Cut out the coloured photocopies of copymaster 27 into the two boards and twenty-four coloured discs.
d) Cover all the pieces in transparent adhesive plastic.

To use the activity
1   The coloured discs (apples) are placed on the trees.
2   Each child has a board on the table in front of him or her.
3   The first child throws the die and collects an apple of the colour shown on the die. This is then placed in the appropriate position on his board.
4   The second child then takes his or her turn in the same way. If there is no space on the board for the colour shown on the die then the child misses that turn.
5   The game continues in this way until one child fills his or her board.

Colour snap
Copymasters 42–3

Objective of the activity
To present colour vocabulary in a meaningful and repetitive way.
   An activity for two children.

Preparation
a) Two photocopies of both copymasters 42 and 43 are needed.
b) Colour copymaster 43 to match the colours shown on copymaster 42.
c) Cut out and cover the cards as in the General instructions.

To use the activity
1   The cards are mixed up and divided between the children.
2   Each child places their stack face down in front of them.
3   The first child begins taking his or her top card and places it face up on the table.
4   The other child then does the same. If the two cards match, word to word, picture to picture or word to picture the children say snap. The first to do so collects all the cards from the central pile.
5   The game continues in this way until one child has collected all the cards.

These cards can also be used for word matching.

Track board games

Object of the activity

The aim of these games is to present a chosen vocabulary in a repetitive way.

This series of games includes: The Teddy track game (copymasters 24–5), Pirate Island (copymasters 94–5), The race track (copymasters 104–5) and The planet race (copymasters 146–7).

Equipment needed

A pot of coloured counters and a die.

Preparation

a) Photocopy the two copymasters required, together with a set of vocabulary cards.

b) Colour the sheets.

c) Trim the sheets and join them together using adhesive tape.

d) Cut out the vocabulary cards.

e) Cover the board and vocabulary cards in transparent adhesive plastic.

To use the activity

The activity may be either a single circuit of the board or several circuits. A counter is needed for each circuit.

1 Each child chooses counters of a different colour, the number of counters being the number of circuits around the track and so dependent on the time available. The counters are laid out in front of the children. The die is thrown by each child to determine who begins.

2 The first child places his or her counter at the start and reads the top vocabulary card. If it is read correctly he or she shakes the die and moves forward the number shown. If the card is not read correctly that turn is missed.

3 The next child then takes his or her turn.

4 When the counter completes the circuit it is placed in the home grid on the base board and the next counter belonging to the child is used.

5 The winner is the first child to have all his or her counters in the home grid.

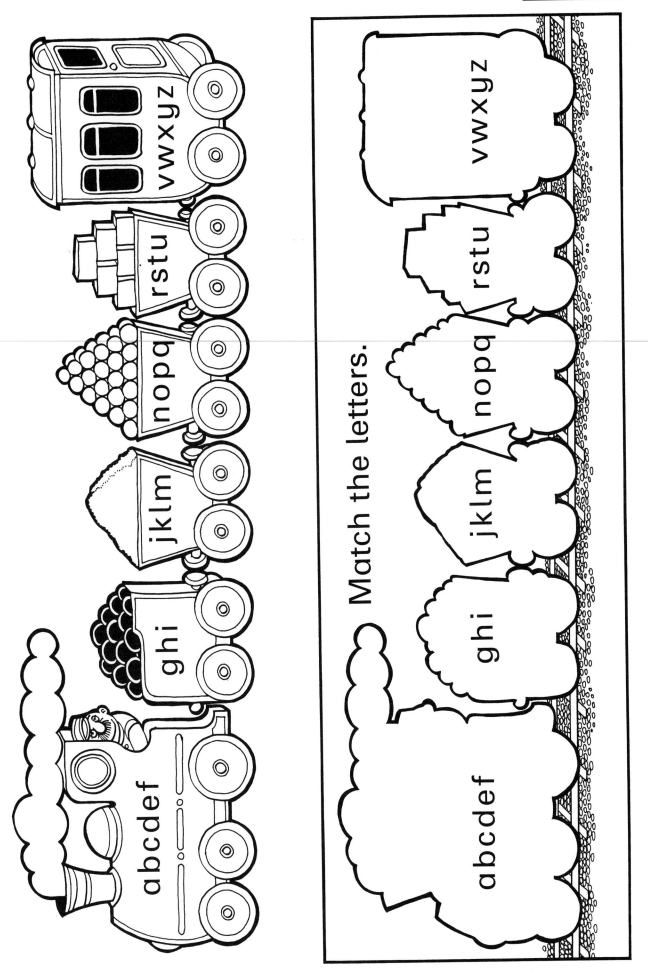

Match the letters.

vwxyz
rstu
nopq
jklm
ghi
abcdef

General Level

Soldier Sam

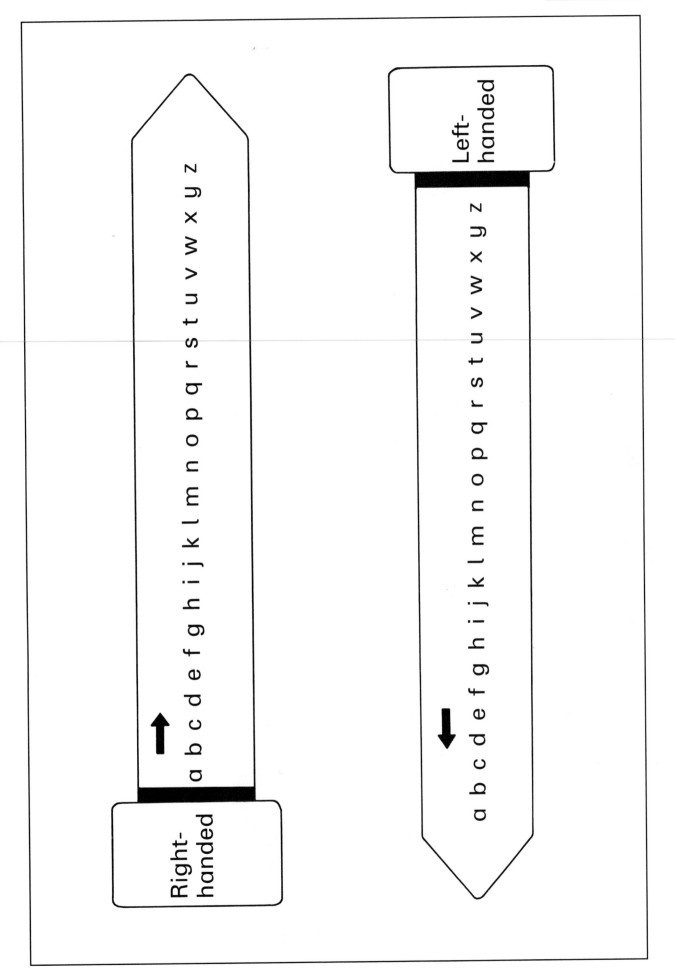

Right-handed

a b c d e f g h i j k l m n o p q r s t u v w x y z

Left-handed

a b c d e f g h i j k l m n o p q r s t u v w x y z

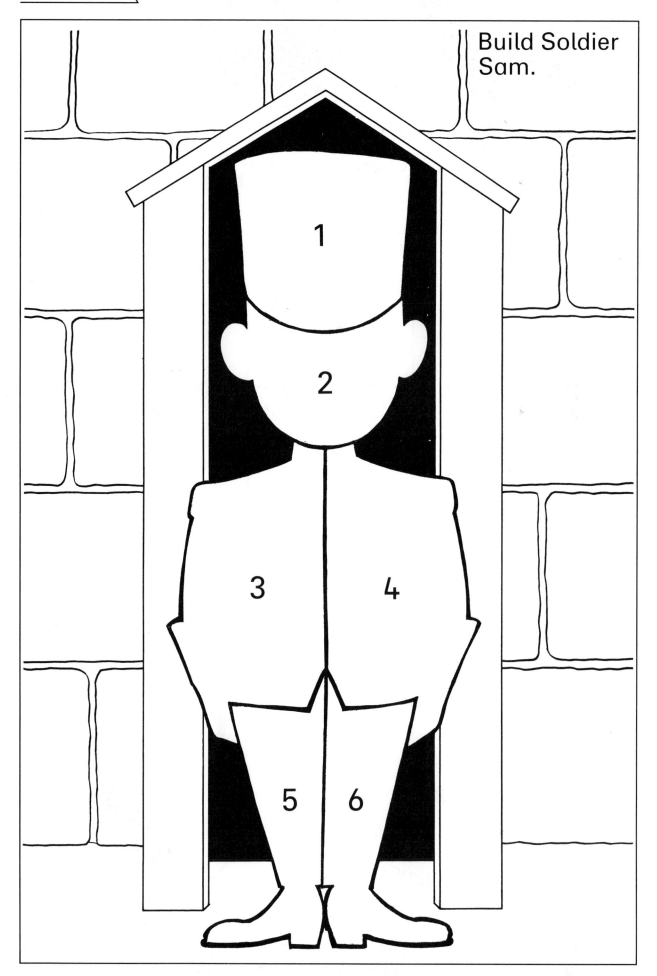

Build Soldier Sam.

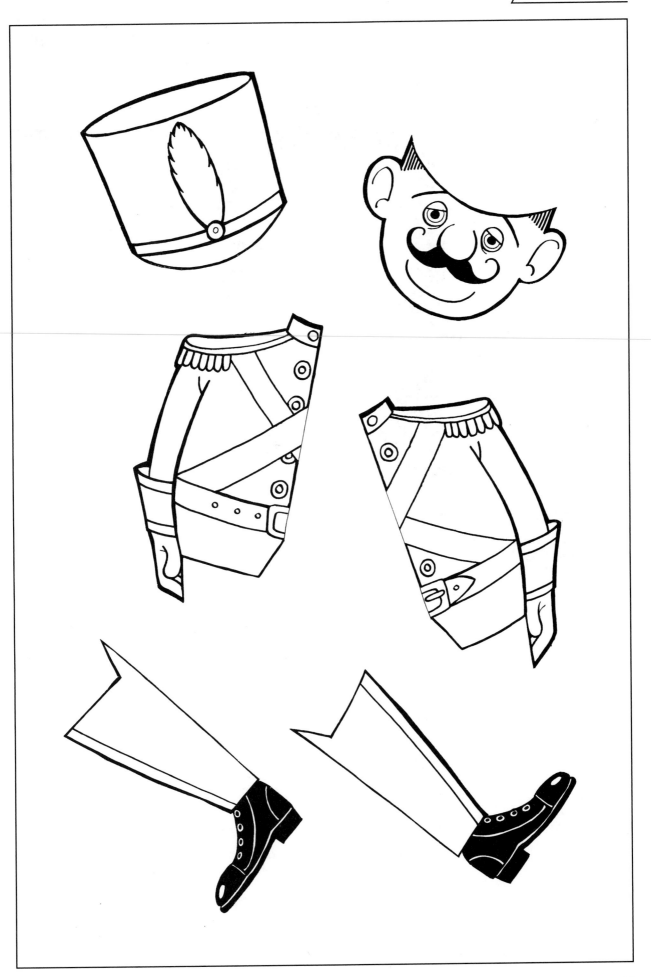

Build the train.

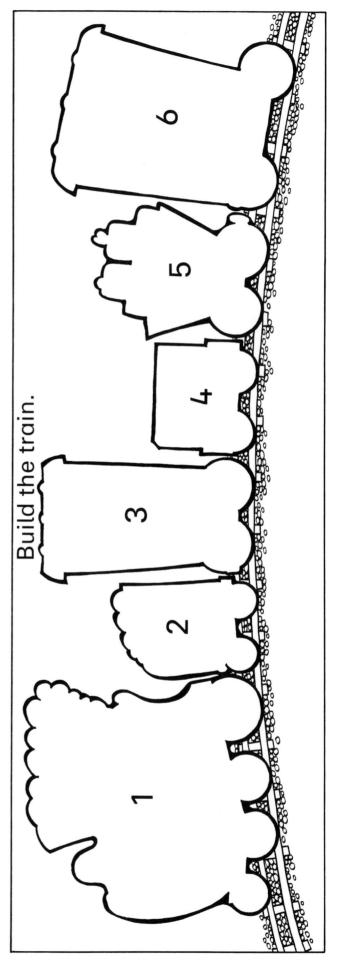

red

bus

hat

roof

house

door

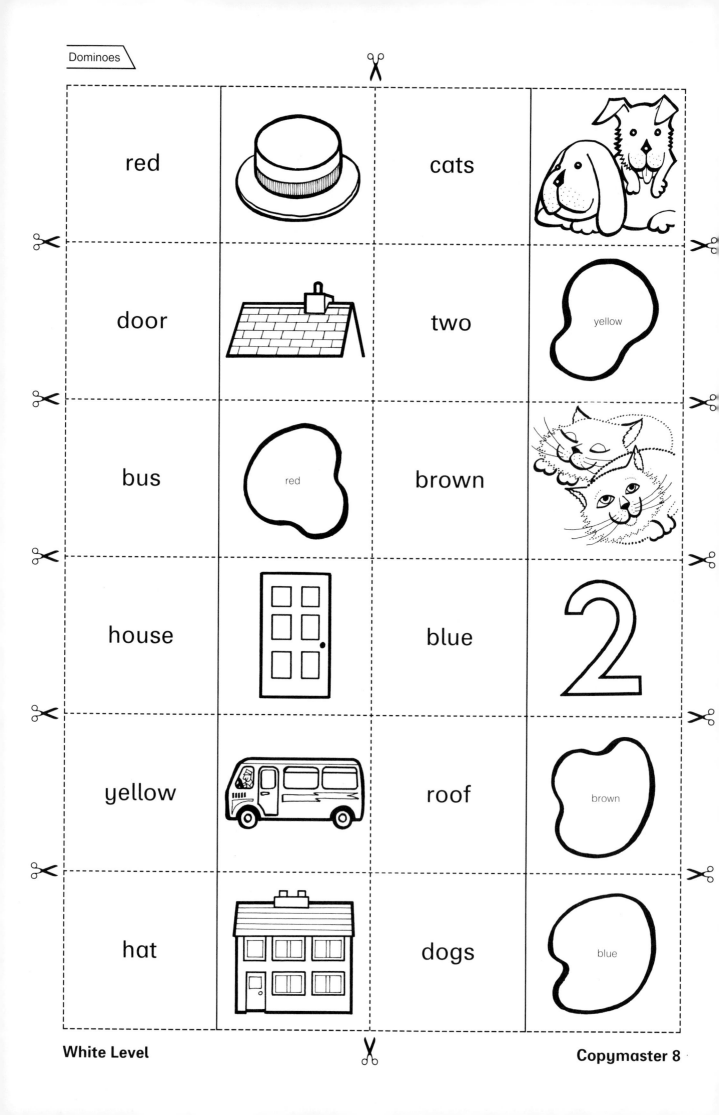

red | cats

door | two

bus | brown

house | blue

yellow | roof

hat | dogs

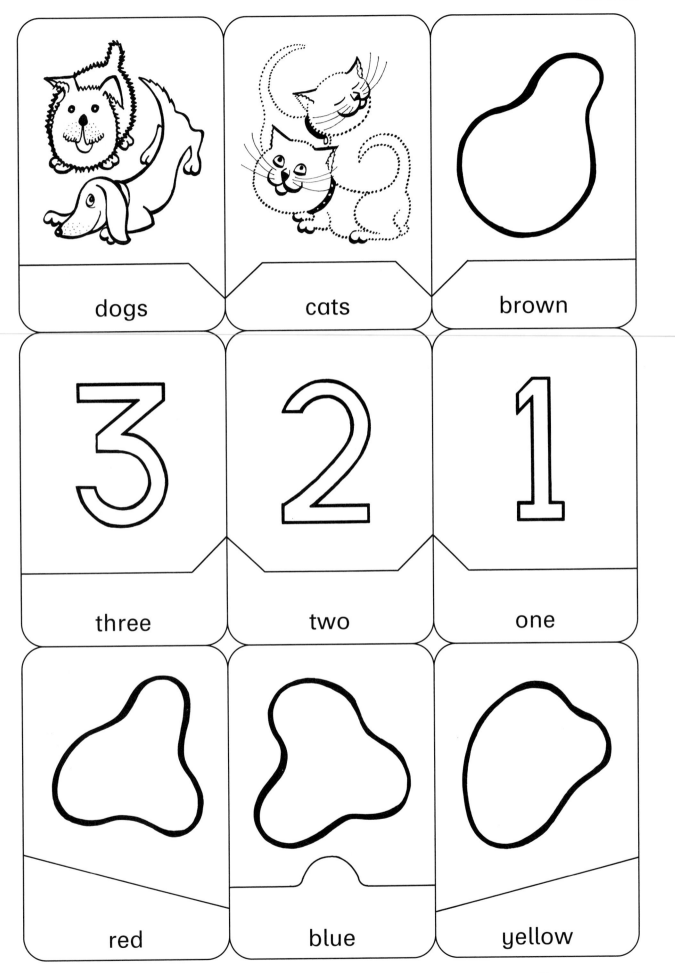

dogs

cats

brown

three

two

one

red

blue

yellow

White Level

little
dog

big
dog

little
house

big
house

man

hat

big house		brown	
man		frog	
little dog		bed	brown
big dog		green	
pond		little house	
hat		mouse	green

mouse

brown

pond

three

up

green

frog

saw

bed

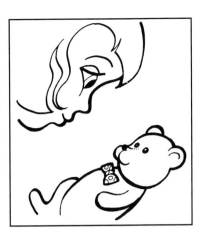

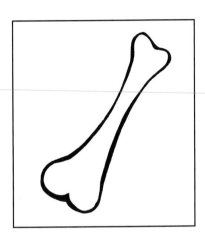

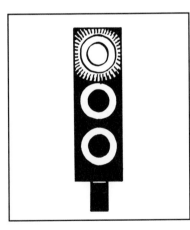

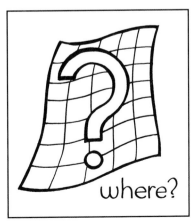

where?

here

White Level

Copymaster 13

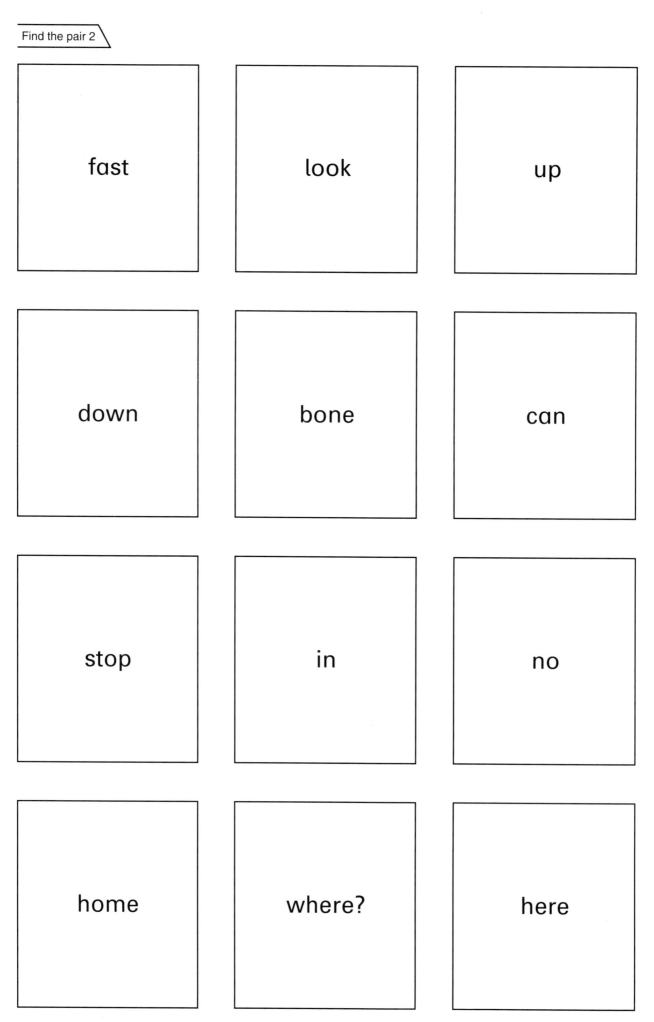

fast	look	up
down	bone	can
stop	in	no
home	where?	here

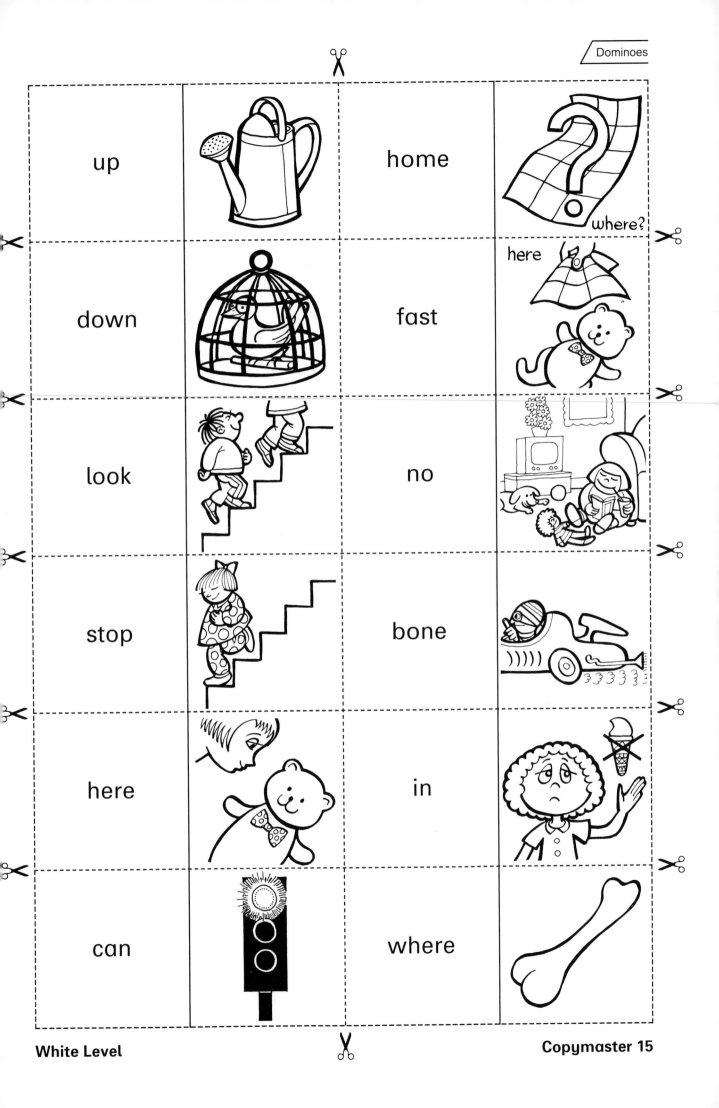

up	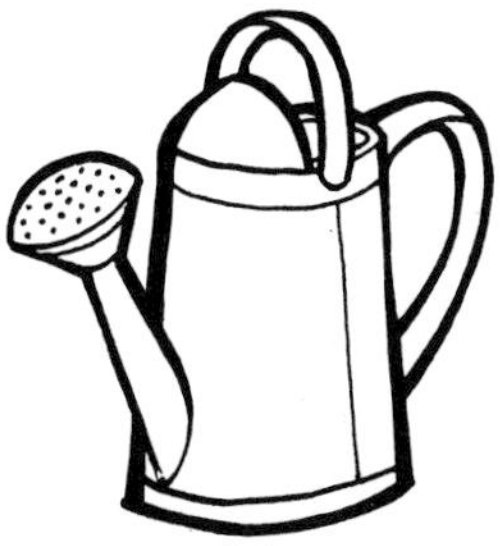	home	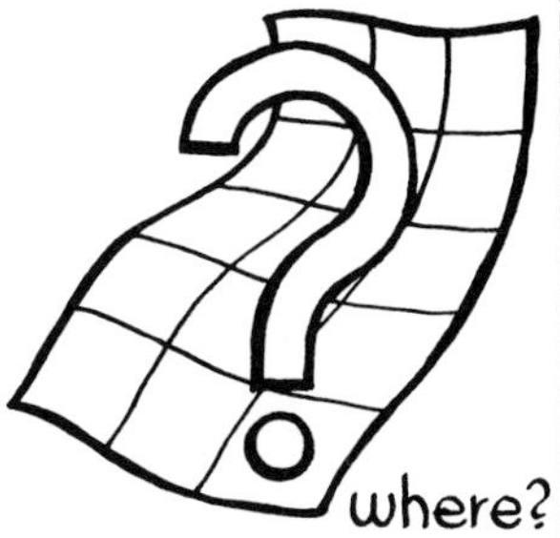
down	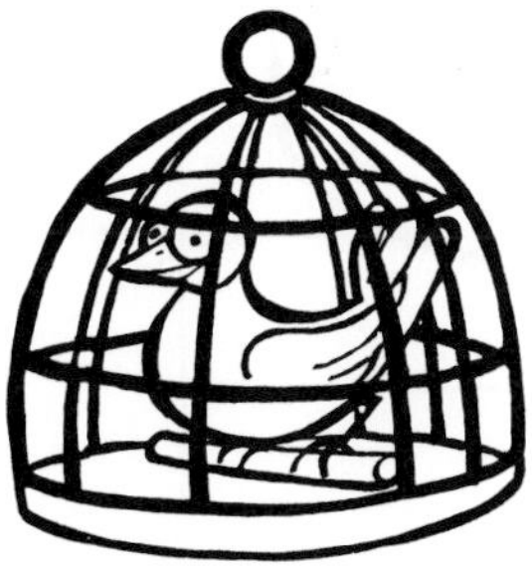	fast	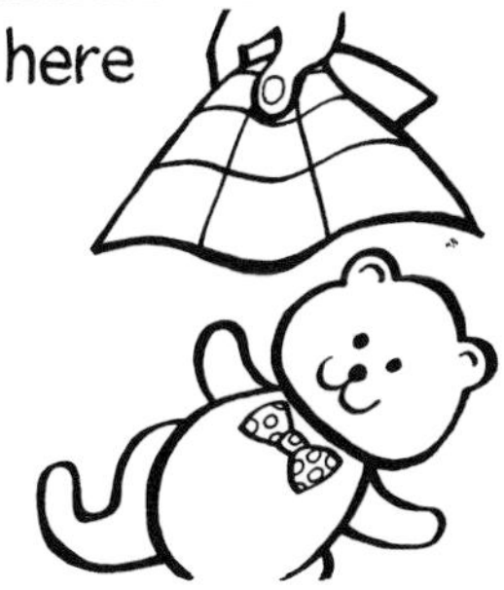
look	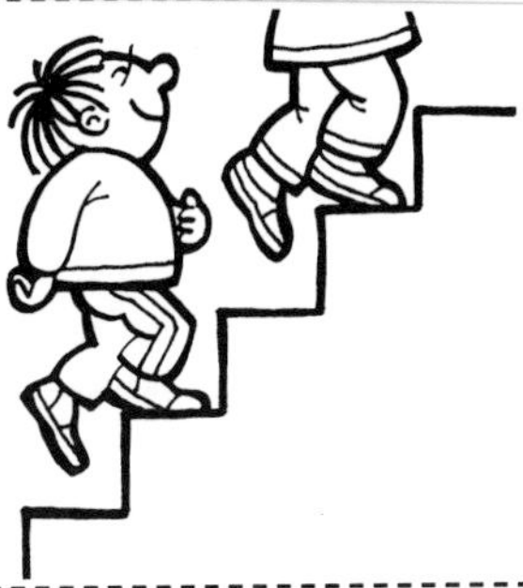	no	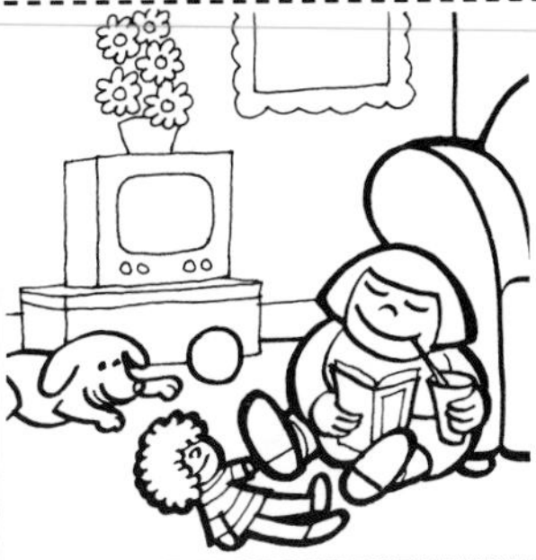
stop	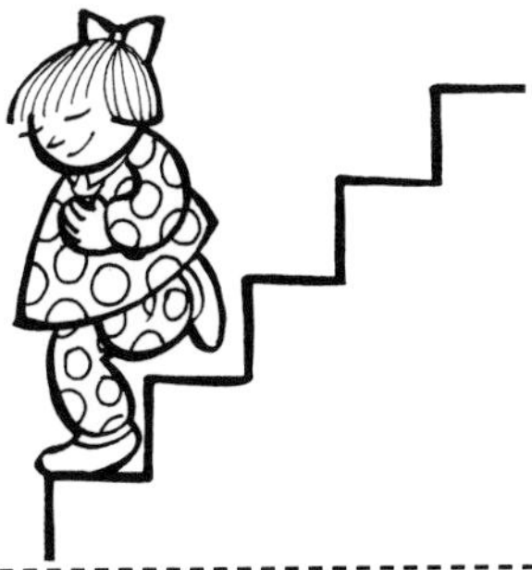	bone	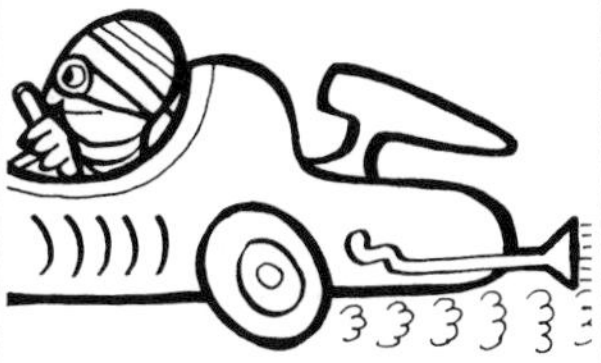
here	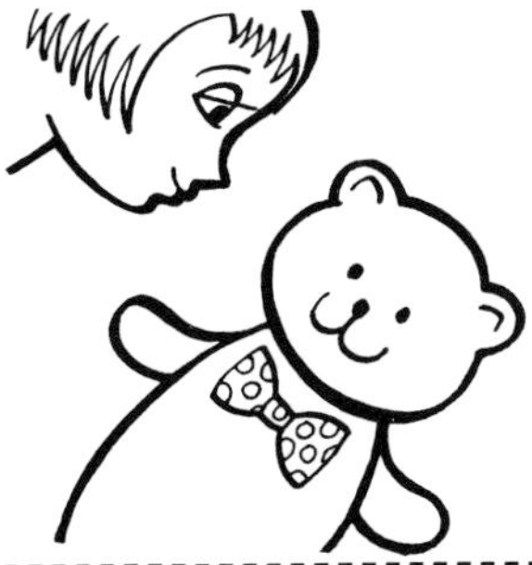	in	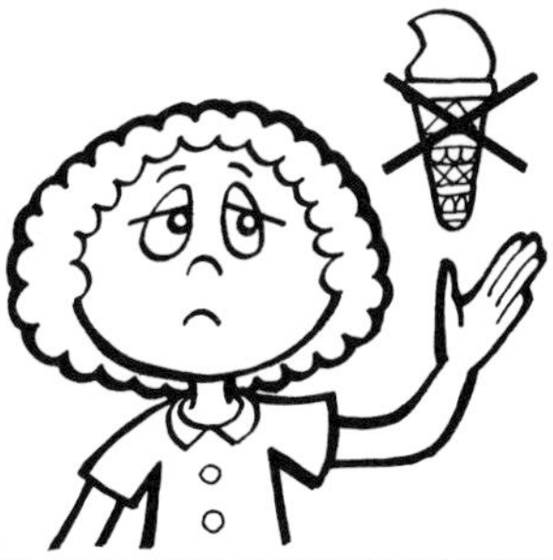
can	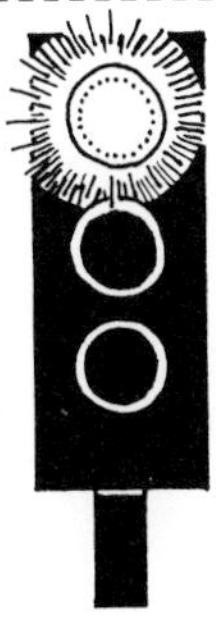	where	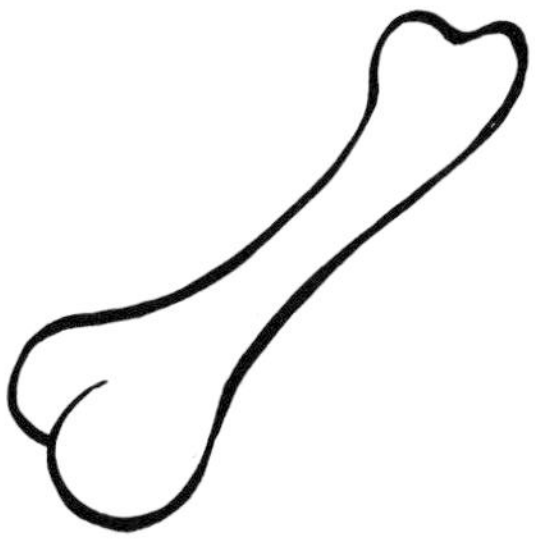

where

in

can

bone

up

down

look

here

no

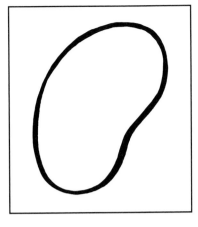
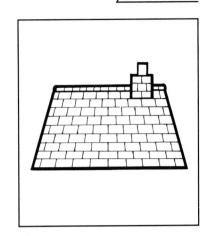

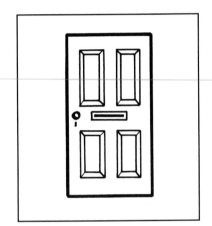
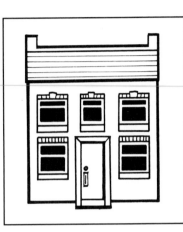
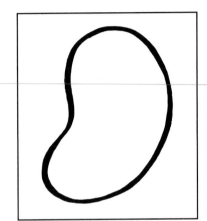

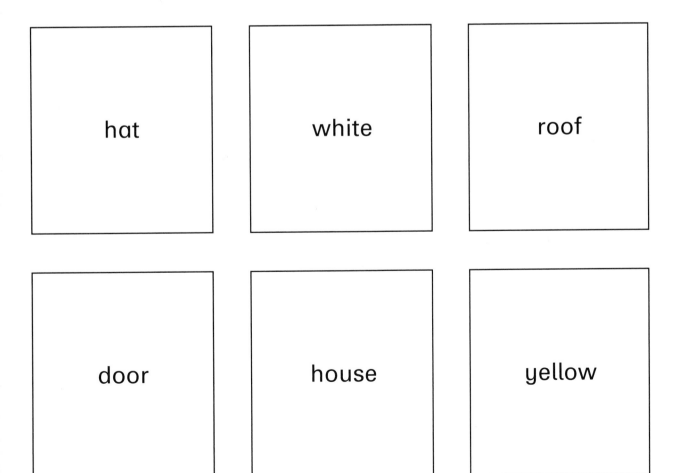

hat	white	roof
door	house	yellow

village	3	window	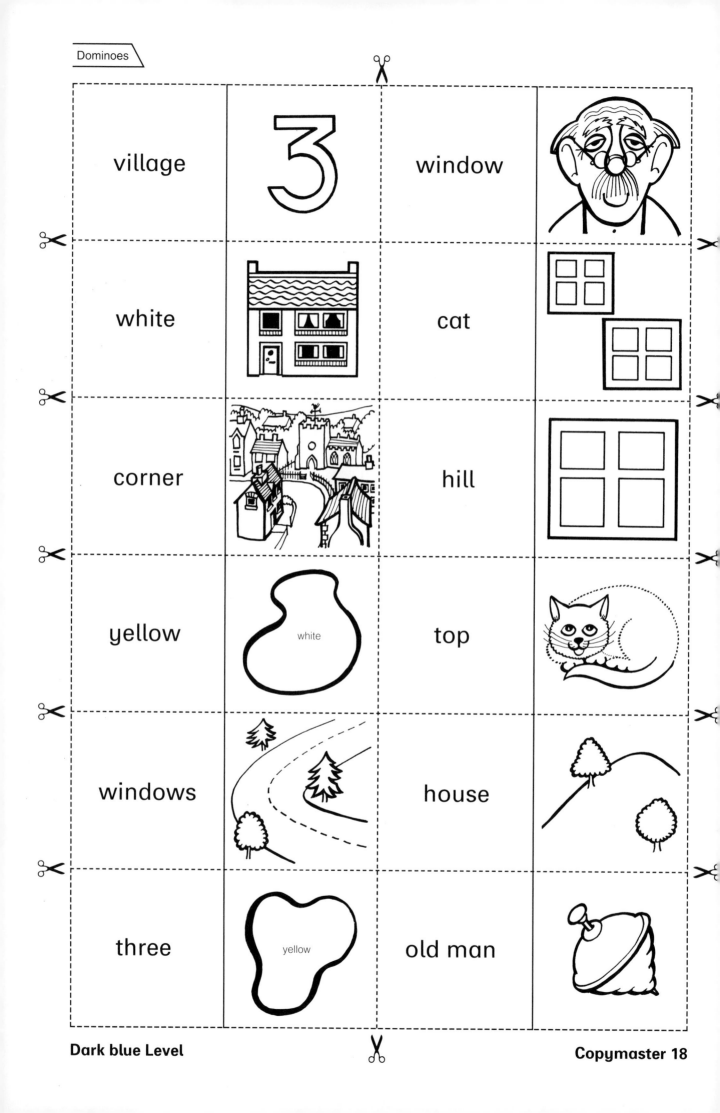
white		cat	
corner		hill	
yellow	white	top	
windows		house	
three	yellow	old man	

cat

top

window

village

white

old man

three

yellow

hill

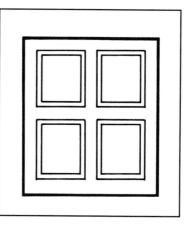

hill	window	windows

old man	top	cat

Match the words.

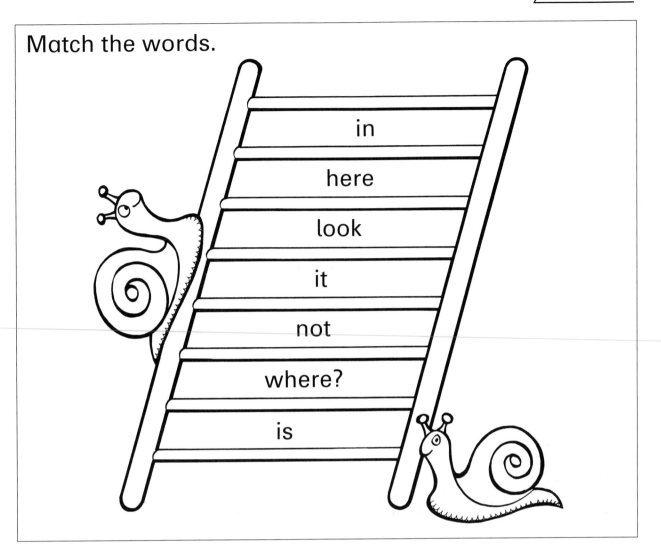

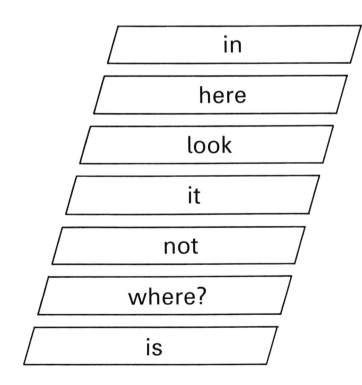

Build Teddy.

Home
grid

The Teddy Bears' picnic

Reading cards

to the woods

start

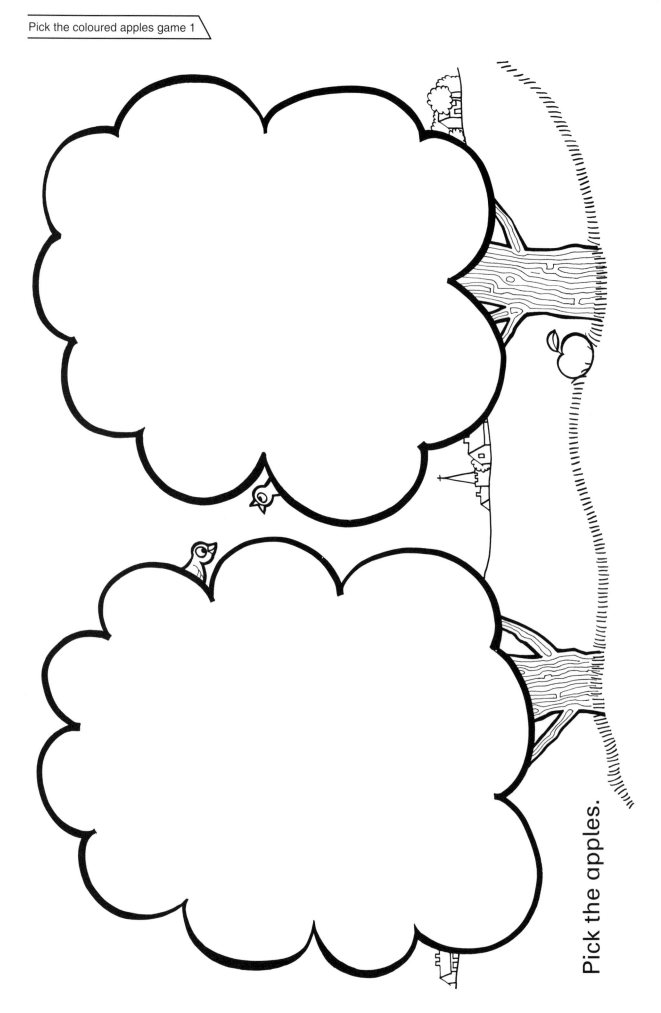

Pick the apples.

yellow	white	yellow	white
blue	green	blue	green
red	brown	red	brown

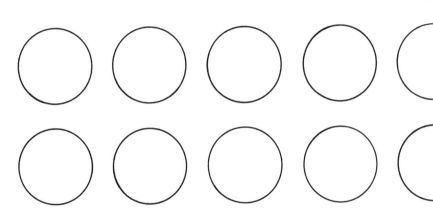

brown	yellow	brown	yellow
green	white	green	white
blue	red	blue	red

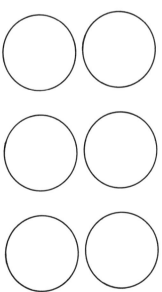

General Level

Copymaster 27

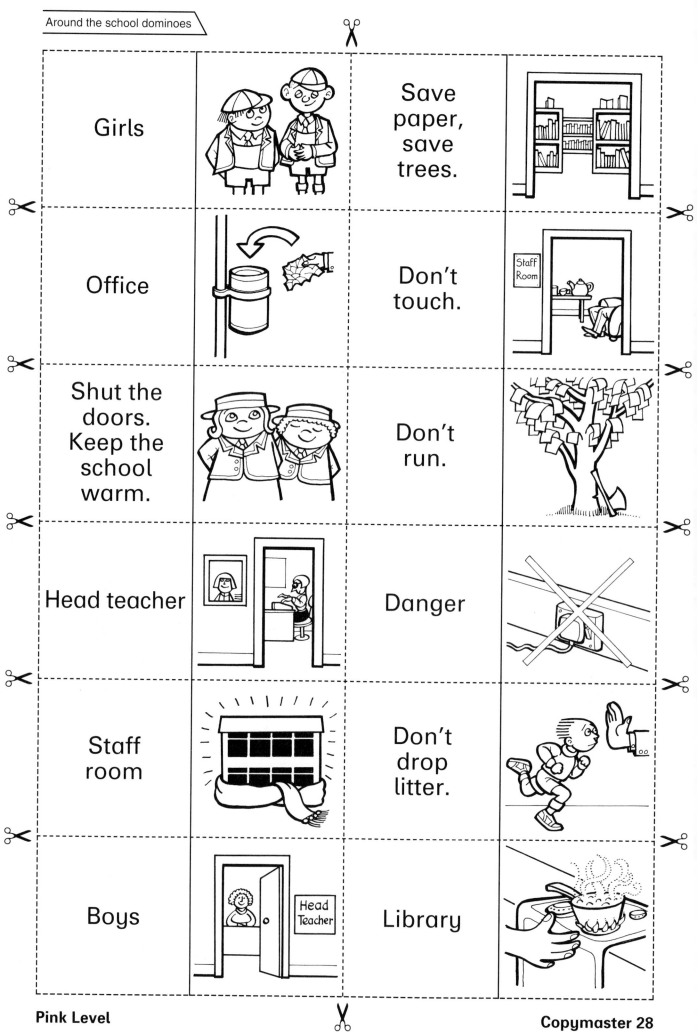

Girls		Save paper, save trees.	
Office		Don't touch.	
Shut the doors. Keep the school warm.		Don't run.	
Head teacher		Danger	
Staff room		Don't drop litter.	
Boys		Library	

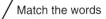

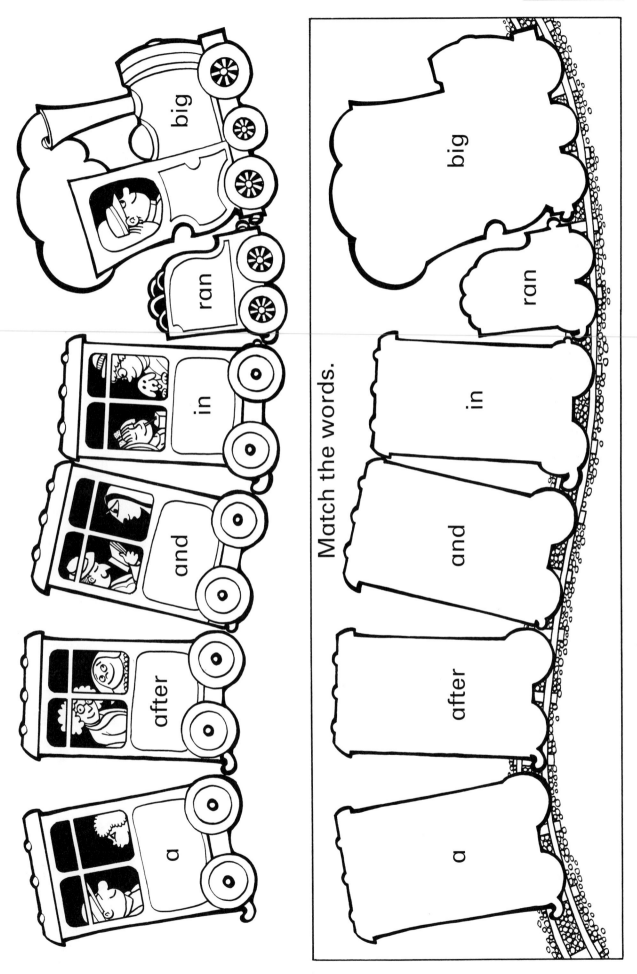

Match the words.

Pink Level

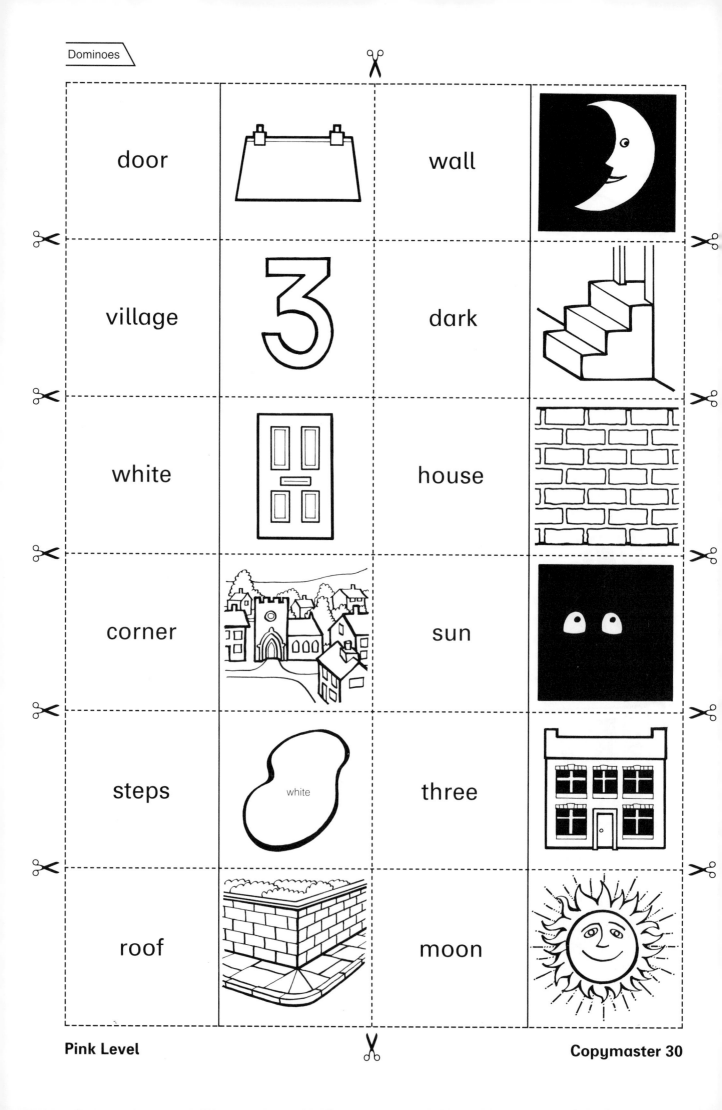

Dominoes

door		wall	
village		dark	
white		house	
corner		sun	
steps	white	three	
roof		moon	

Pink Level

Copymaster 30

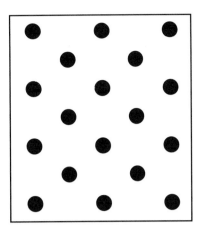

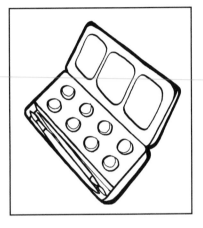

Pink Level

Copymaster 31

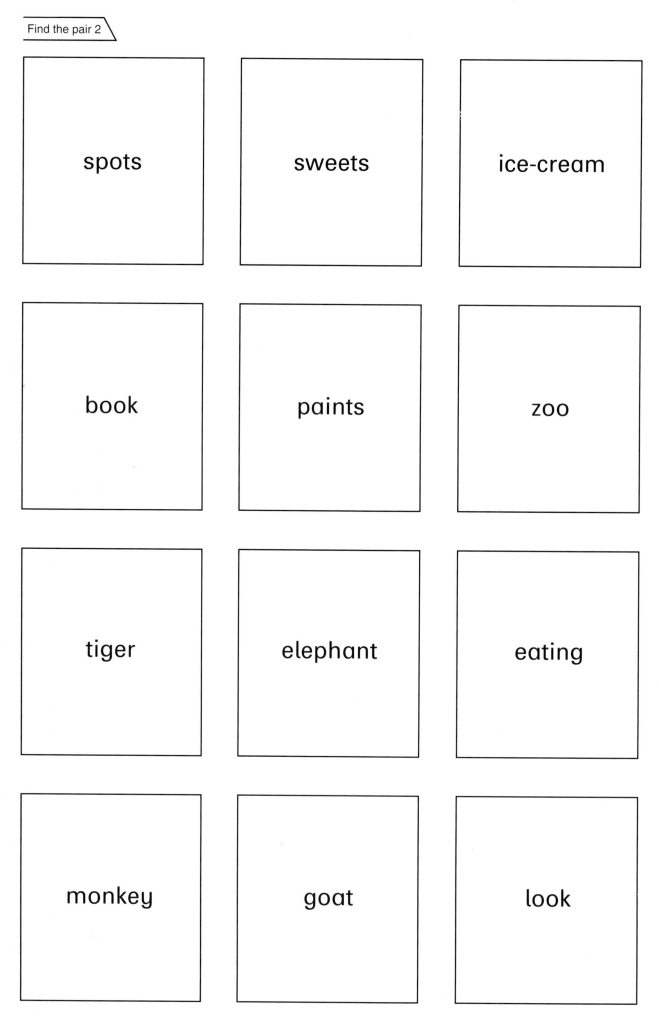

spots	sweets	ice-cream
book	paints	zoo
tiger	elephant	eating
monkey	goat	look

look		painted	
paints	●	eating	
spots		Dad	
ice-cream		run	
coat		spot	
some sweets		Mum	

box

monster

rabbit

cabbage

run

mum

carrot

book

tiger

run		mum	
carrot		tiger	
goat		cabbage	
rabbit		book	
paints		miaow	
monster		box	

cymbals

robber

bell

Happy Birthday

bike

park

house

pan

drum

robber	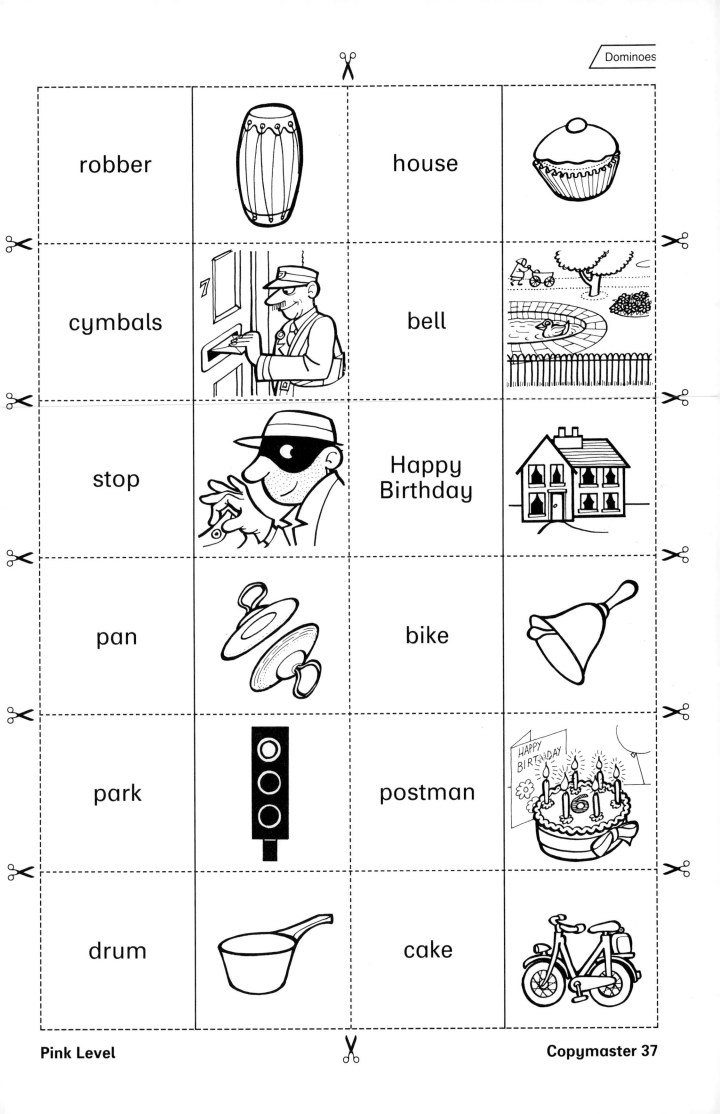	house	
cymbals		bell	
stop		Happy Birthday	
pan		bike	
park		postman	
drum		cake	

down	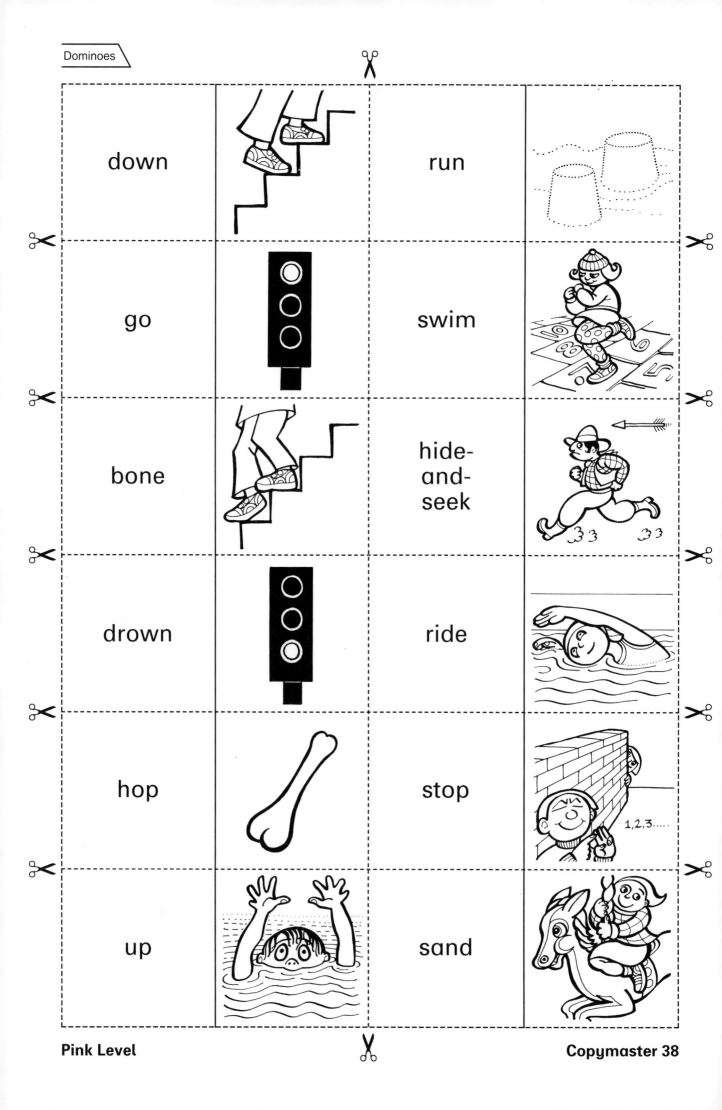	run	
go		swim	
bone		hide-and-seek	
drown		ride	
hop		stop	
up		sand	

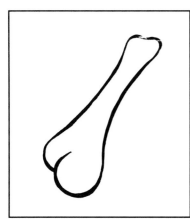

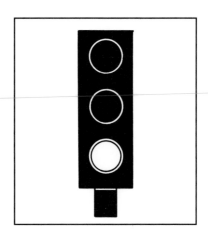
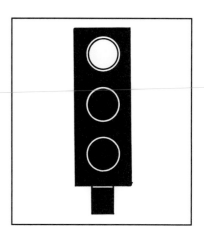

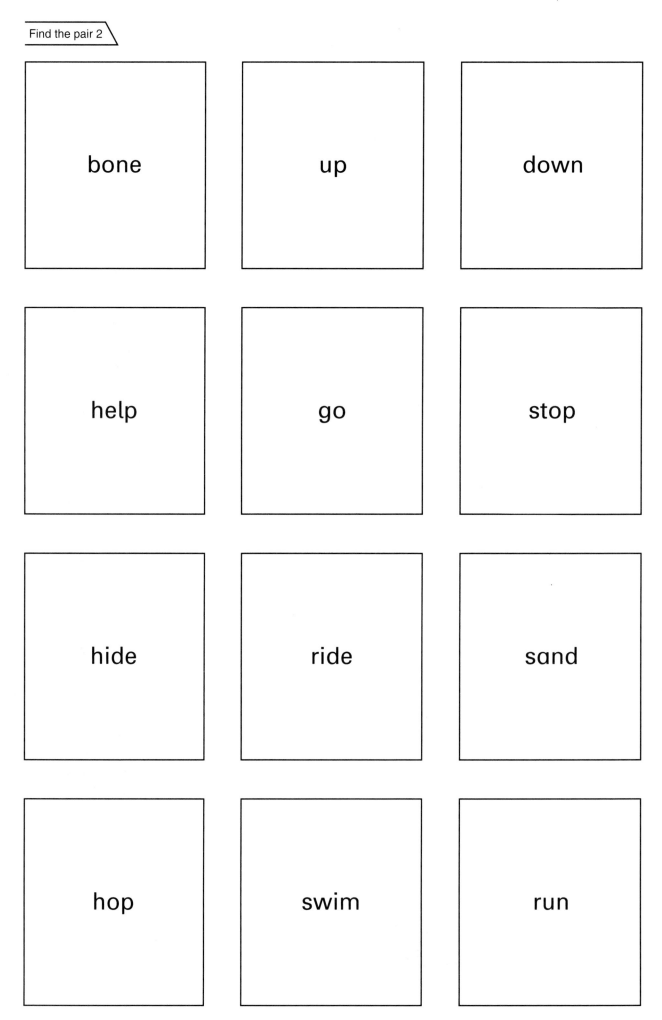

bone	up	down
help	go	stop
hide	ride	sand
hop	swim	run

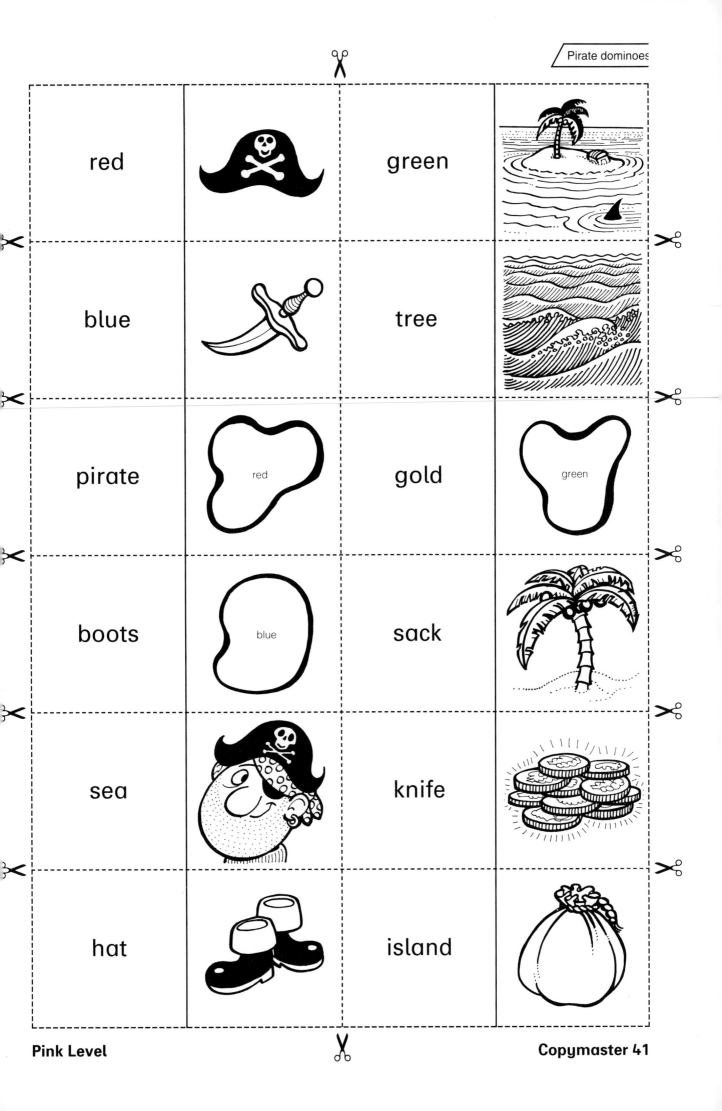

red		green	
blue		tree	
pirate	red	gold	green
boots	blue	sack	
sea		knife	
hat		island	

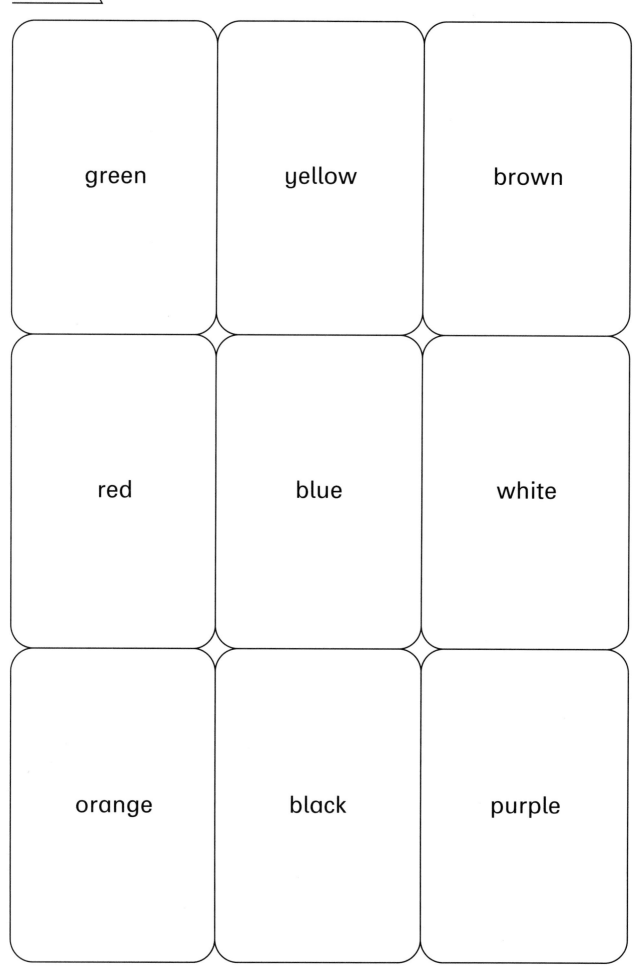

green	yellow	brown
red	blue	white
orange	black	purple

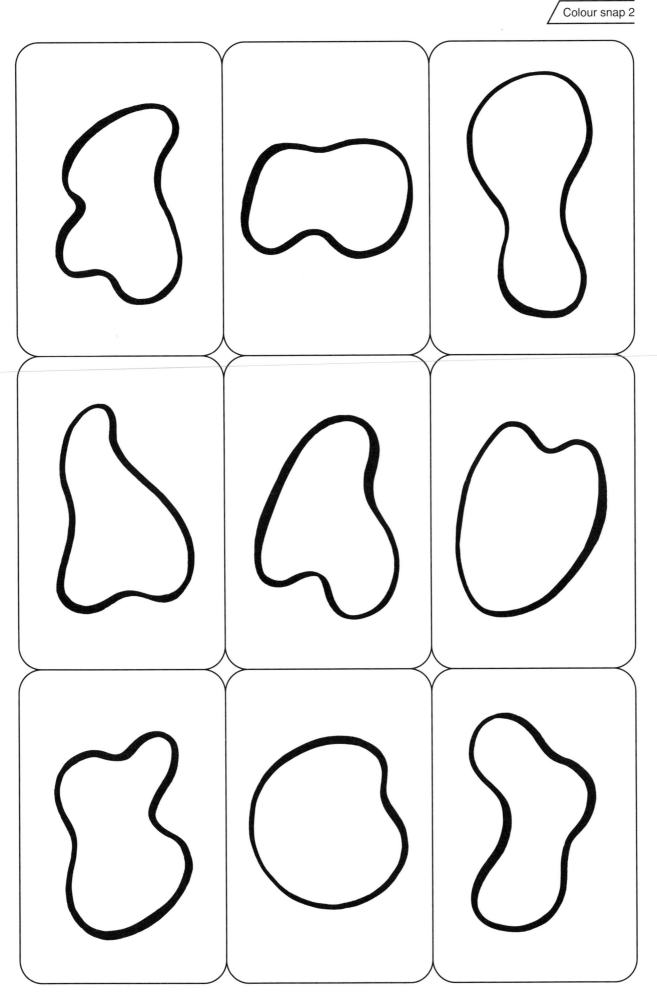

WORD AHOY

MATCH
THE
WORDS

look	go	I	going
in	you	feel	Here
here	see	swing	is
no	fun	all	thing
not	ride	No	tall
where	stop	said	small
is	fast	The	ground
it	don't	its	lost
my	little	all	hit
help	feed	gone	stopped
home	think	more	them
play	want	they	what
come	found	round	mess
out	guess	feel	fix
in	why	sick	come
can	went	are	night

right	went	had	I
fright	want	sailed	can
old	again	deep	hid
sold	can	sky	his
in	made	sea	with
a	this	on	over
along	that	shone	to
had	not	sky	go
gave	gone	in	top
some	on	was	cave
wanted	here	away	rock
got	see	across	sat
There	not	will	watch
eating	where	year	was
saw	whether	day	flew
the	each	me	up

big	look	home	key
ran	hit	saw	
in	I	she	
after	day	to	
and	stay	go	
a	not	by	
He	for	fell	
into	so	shining	
down	as	away	
took	you	all	
an	there	said	
they	will	come	
from	next	look	
fall	got	in	
came	lives	up	
at	hid	around	

Write the words you matched in the waves.

Now write 3 sentences using some of the words you have found.

Draw your own pirate ship on the back of this sheet.

Build Father Christmas.

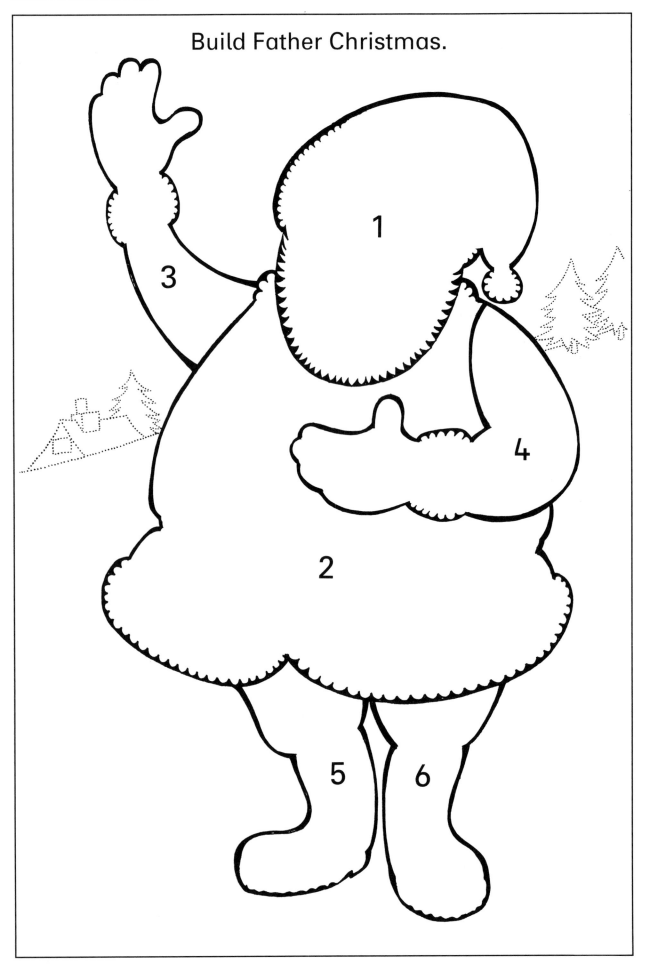

Match the words.

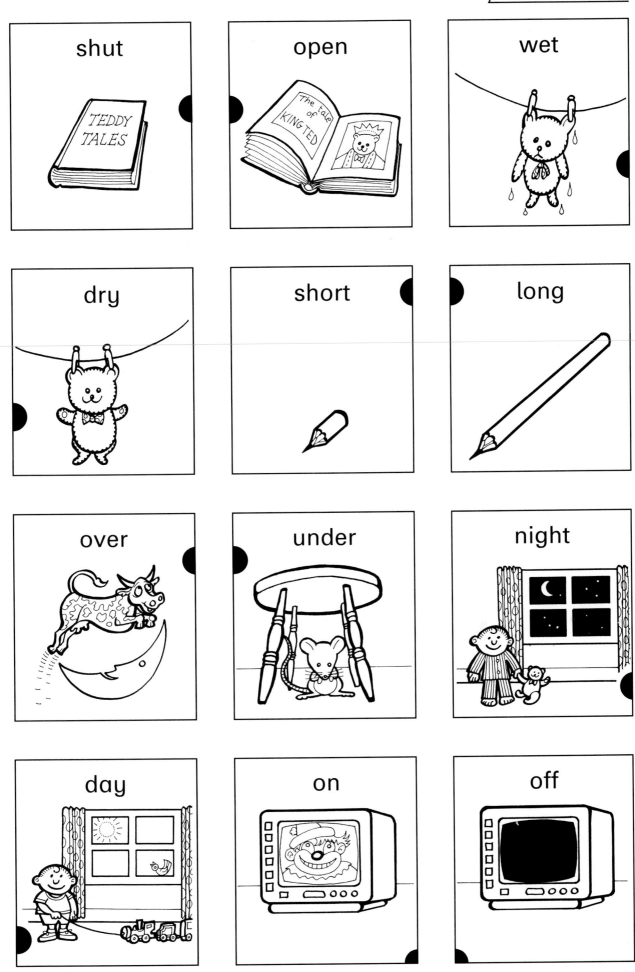

General Level

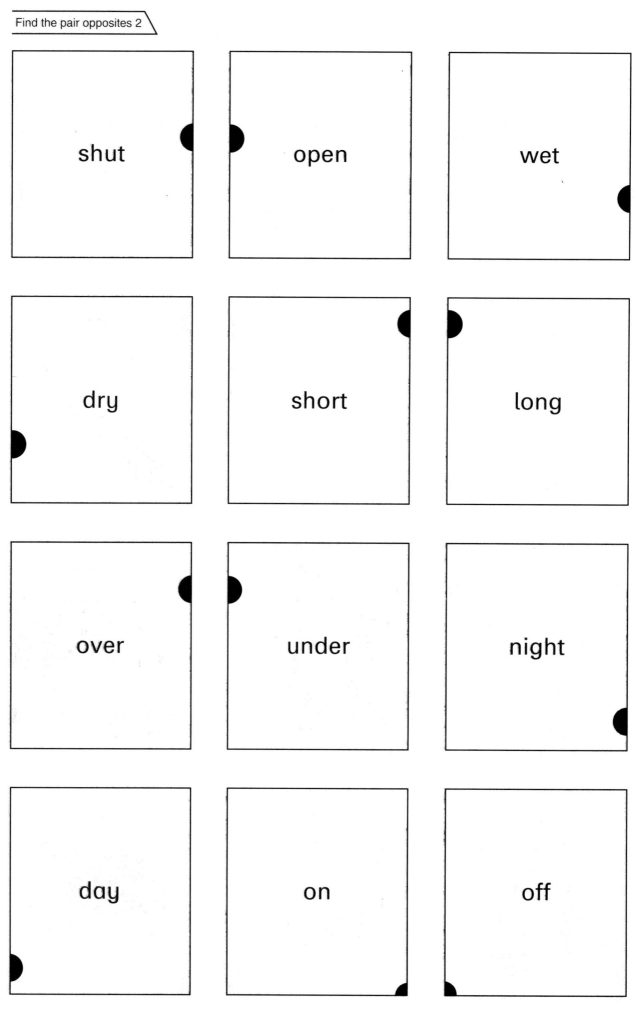

shut

open

wet

dry

short

long

over

under

night

day

on

empty

full

clean

dirty

little

big

happy

sad

white

black

in

out

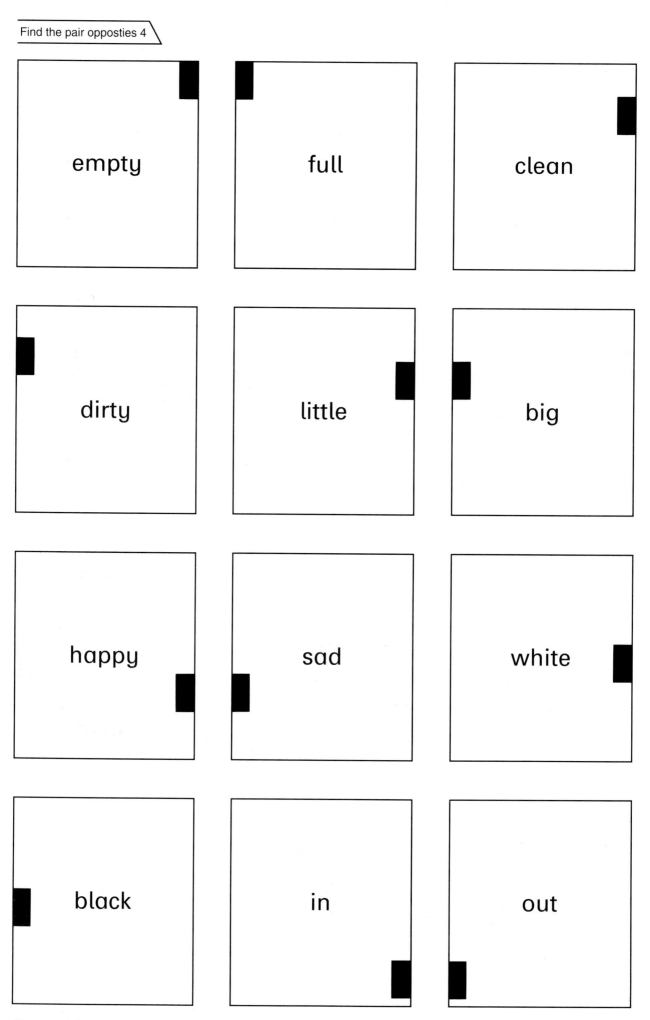

empty

full

clean

dirty

little

big

happy

sad

white

black

in

out

Match the words.

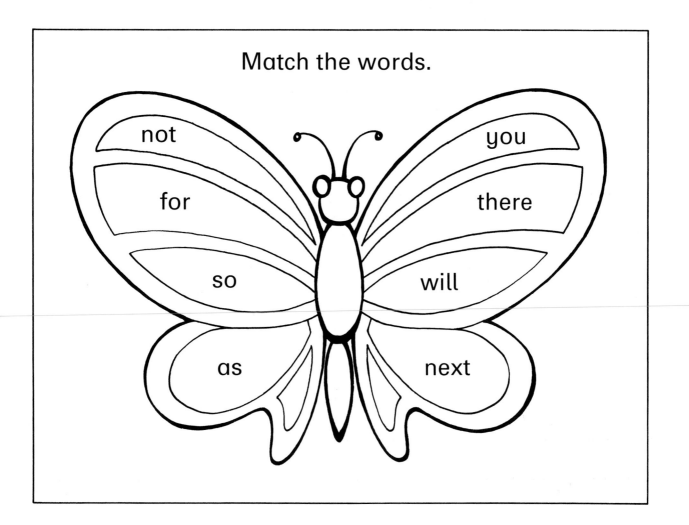

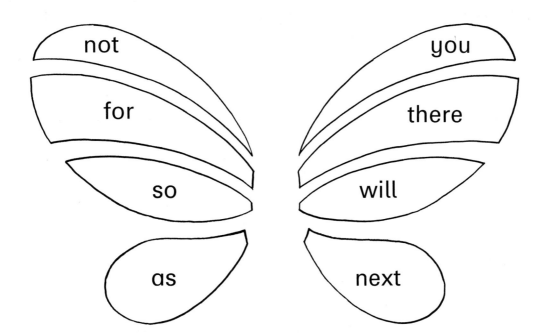

Match the words.

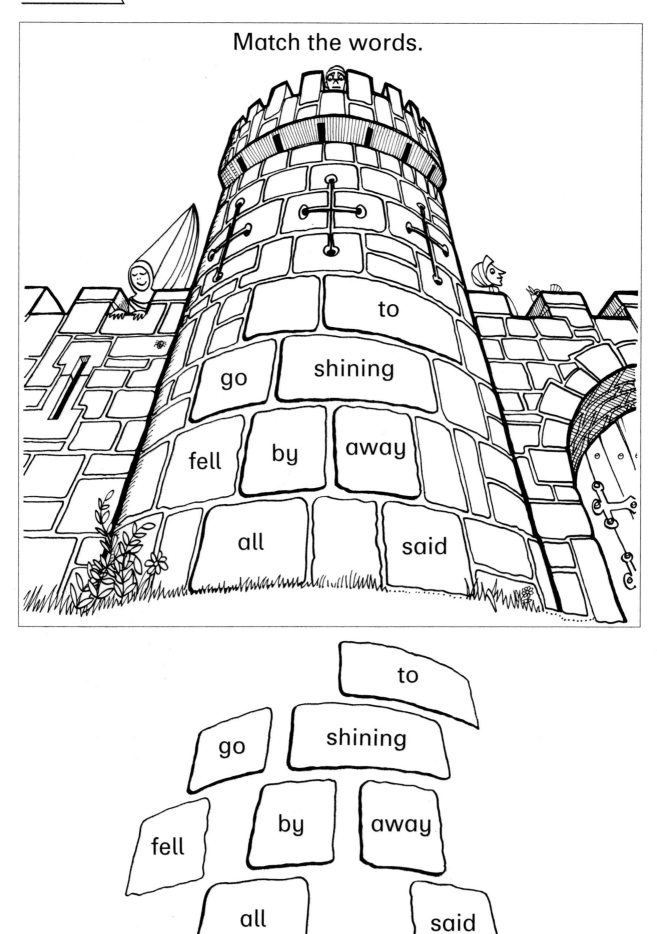

dad	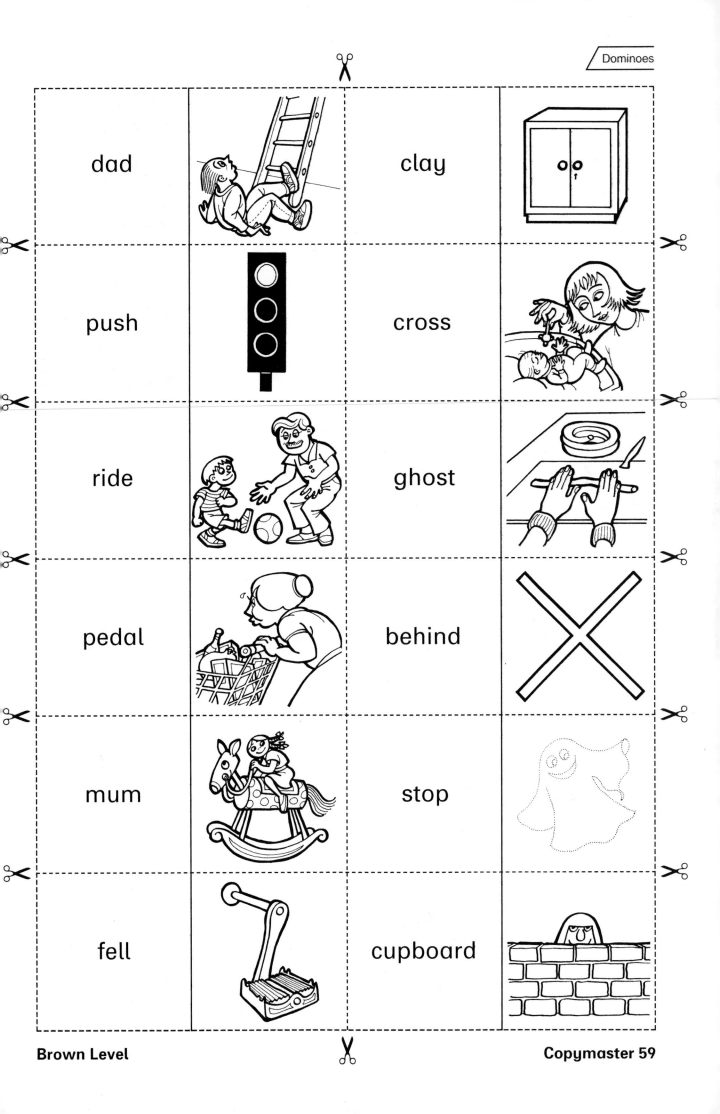	clay	
push		cross	
ride		ghost	
pedal		behind	
mum		stop	
fell		cupboard	

pram	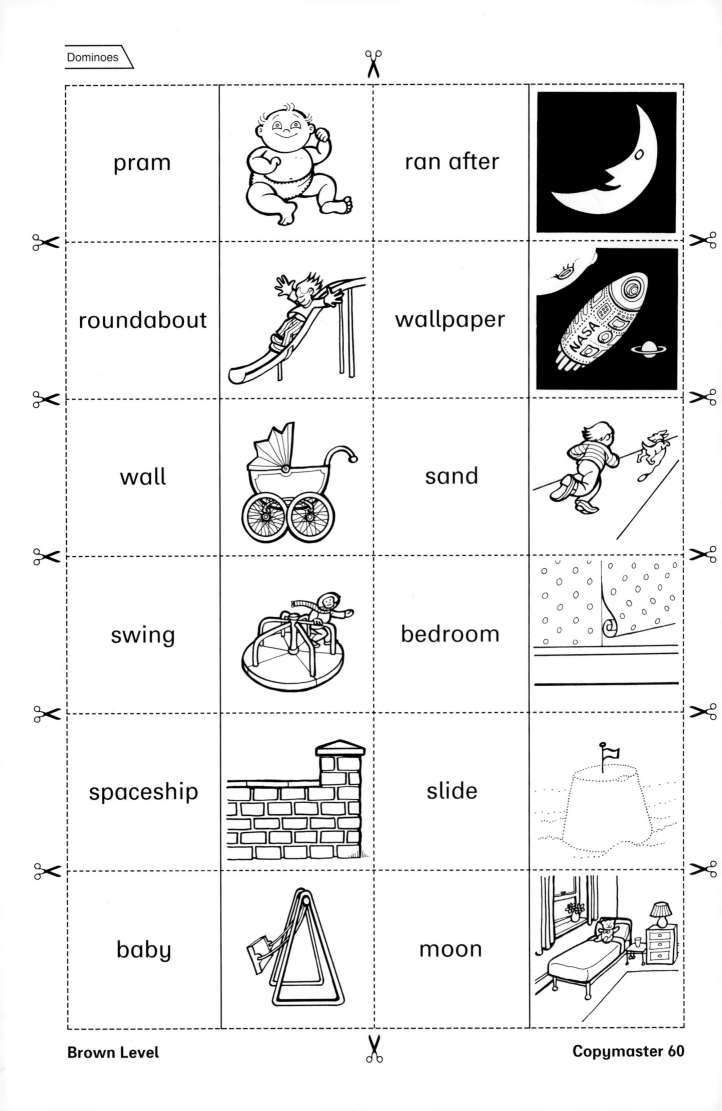	ran after	
roundabout		wallpaper	
wall		sand	
swing		bedroom	
spaceship		slide	
baby		moon	

moon

spaceship

wallpaper

sand

wall

baby

pram

run after

bedroom

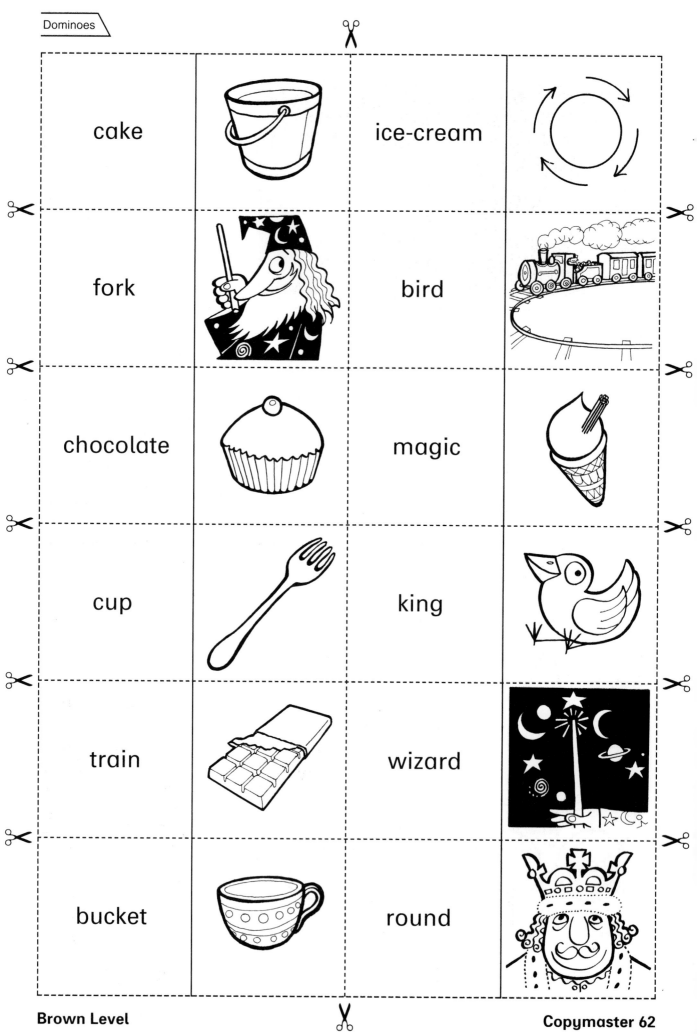

cake		ice-cream	
fork		bird	
chocolate		magic	
cup		king	
train		wizard	
bucket		round	

 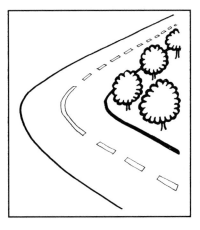 

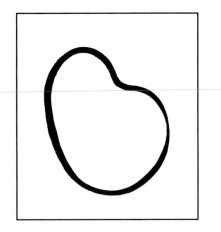 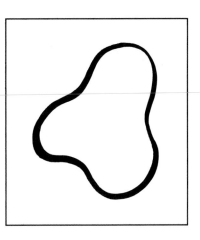 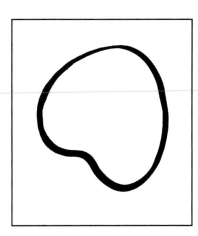

 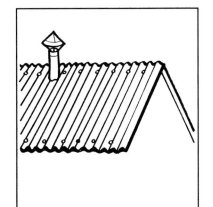 

Brown Level

Copymaster 63

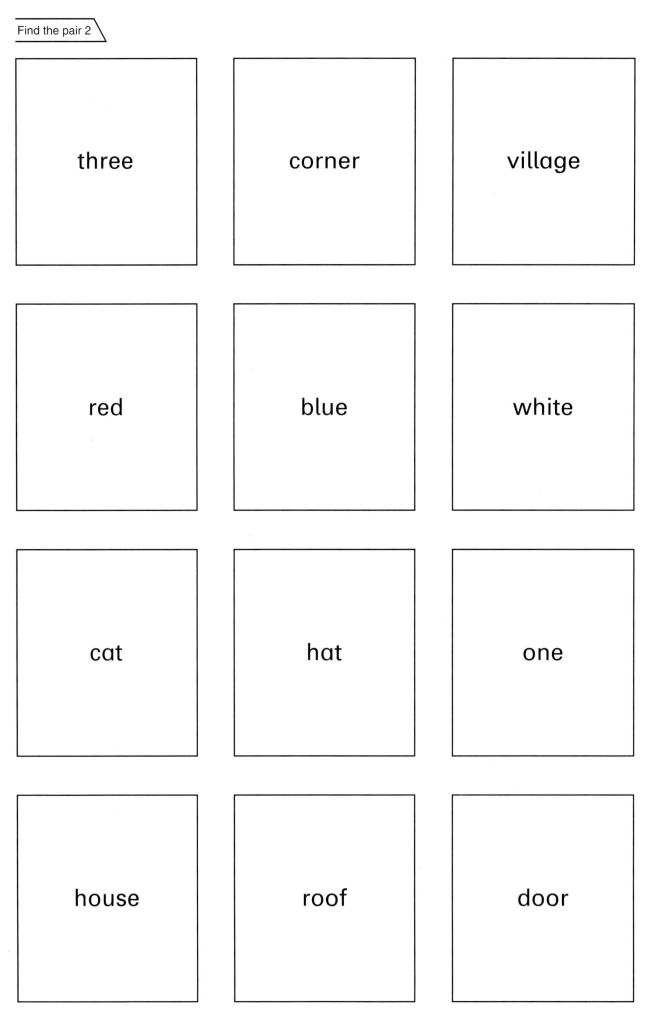

three

corner

village

red

blue

white

cat

hat

one

house

roof

door

house

cat

corner

roof

hat

door

three

village

one

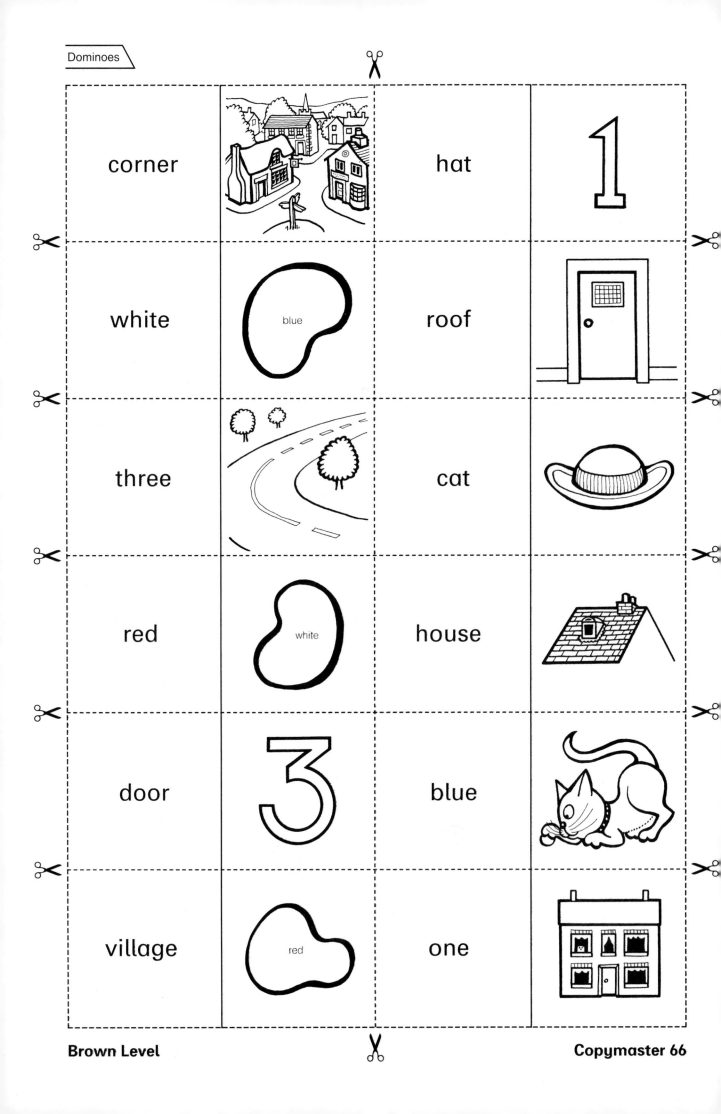

corner		hat	1
white	blue	roof	
three		cat	
red	white	house	
door	3	blue	
village	red	one	

Brown Level

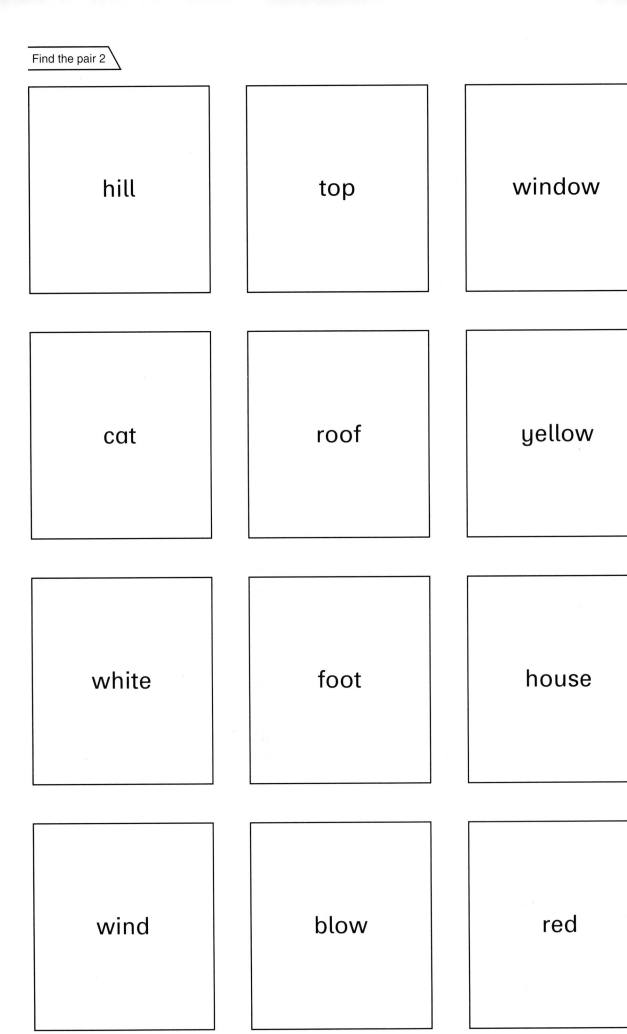

hill

top

window

cat

roof

yellow

white

foot

house

wind

blow

red

hill

top

window

wind

cat

roof

house

foot

white

Match the words.

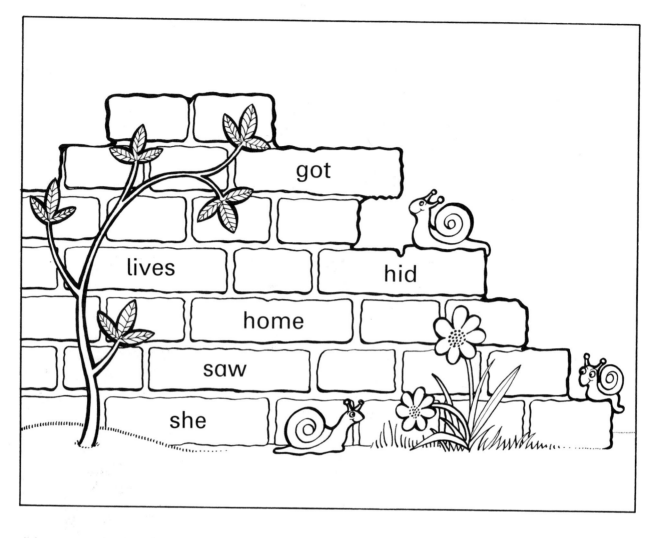

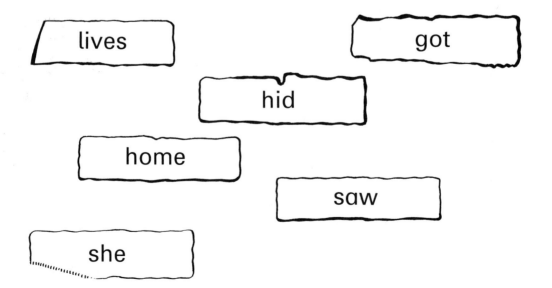

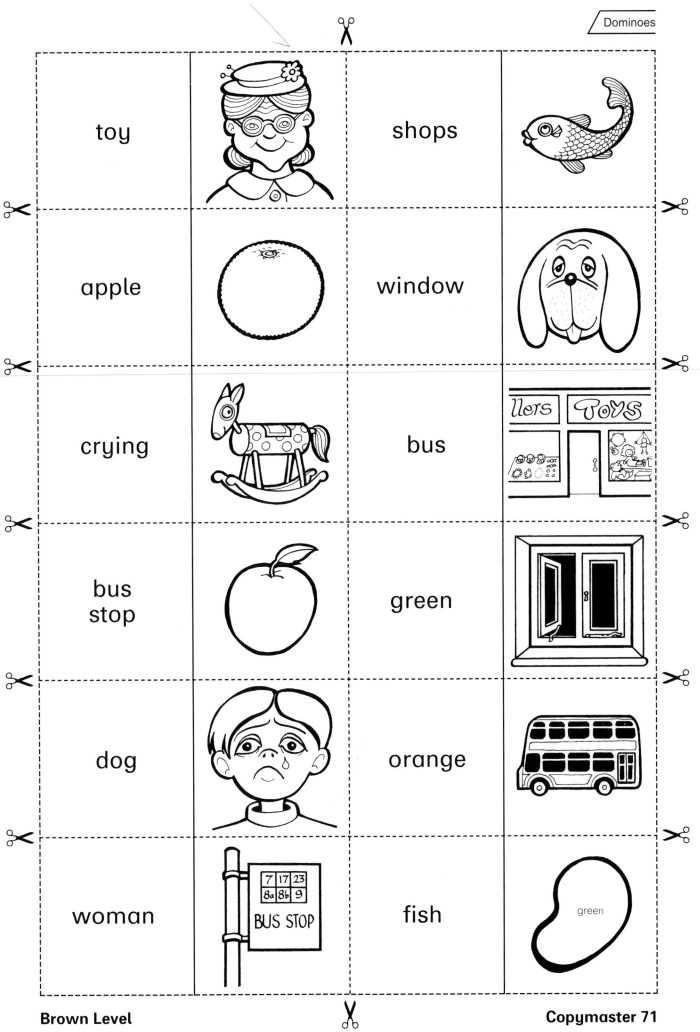

toy		shops	
apple		window	
crying		bus	
bus stop		green	
dog		orange	
woman		fish	

Brown Level

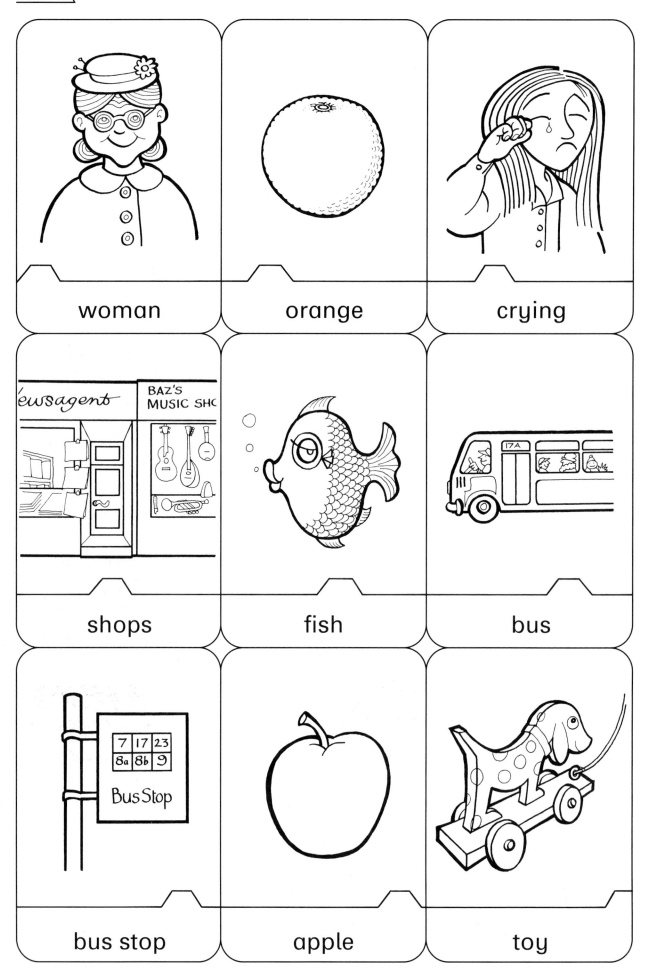

woman

orange

crying

shops

fish

bus

bus stop

apple

toy

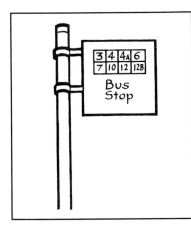

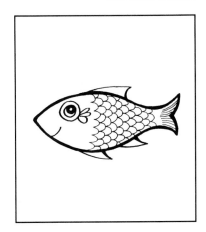

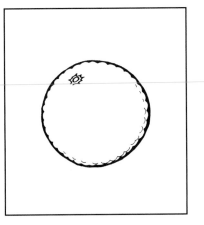

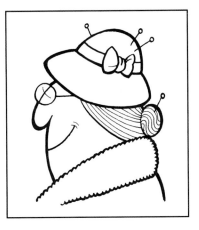

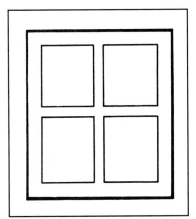

Brown Level

Copymaster 73

bus
stop

crying

fish

apple

orange

shops

toy

old
woman

bus

dog

town

window

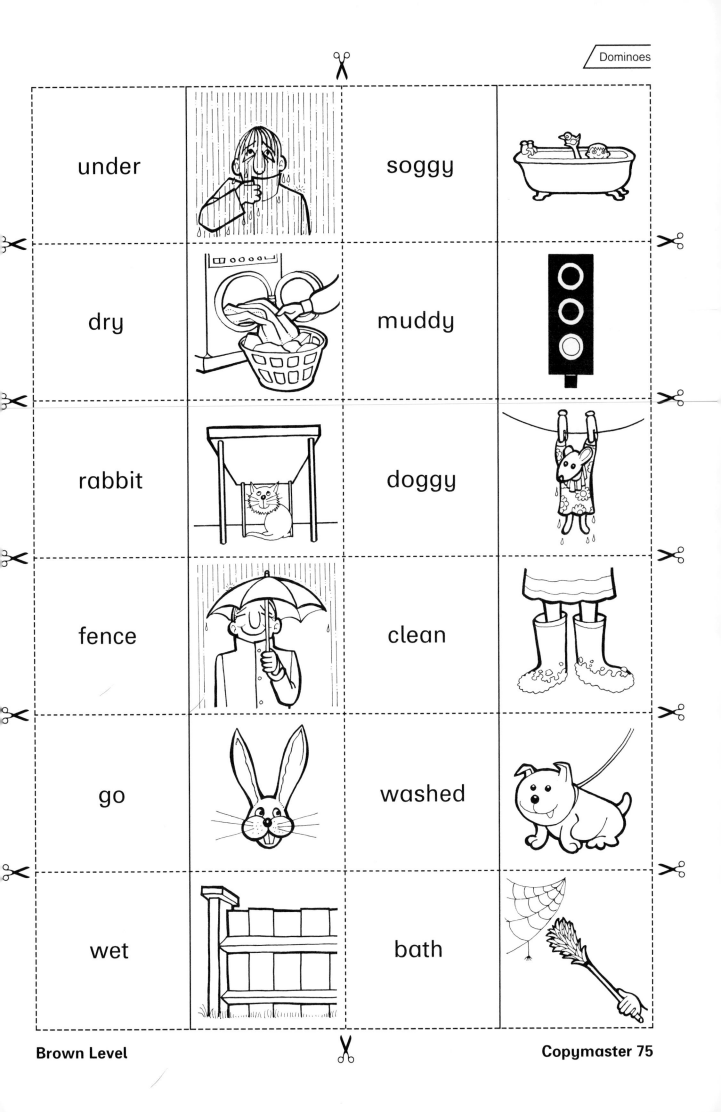

under		soggy	
dry		muddy	
rabbit		doggy	
fence		clean	
go		washed	
wet		bath	

fence

soggy

doggy

bath

wash

dry

muddy

clean

rabbit

water		tray	
books		pull	
washing		sleep	
over		push	
mud		cross	
barked		fire	

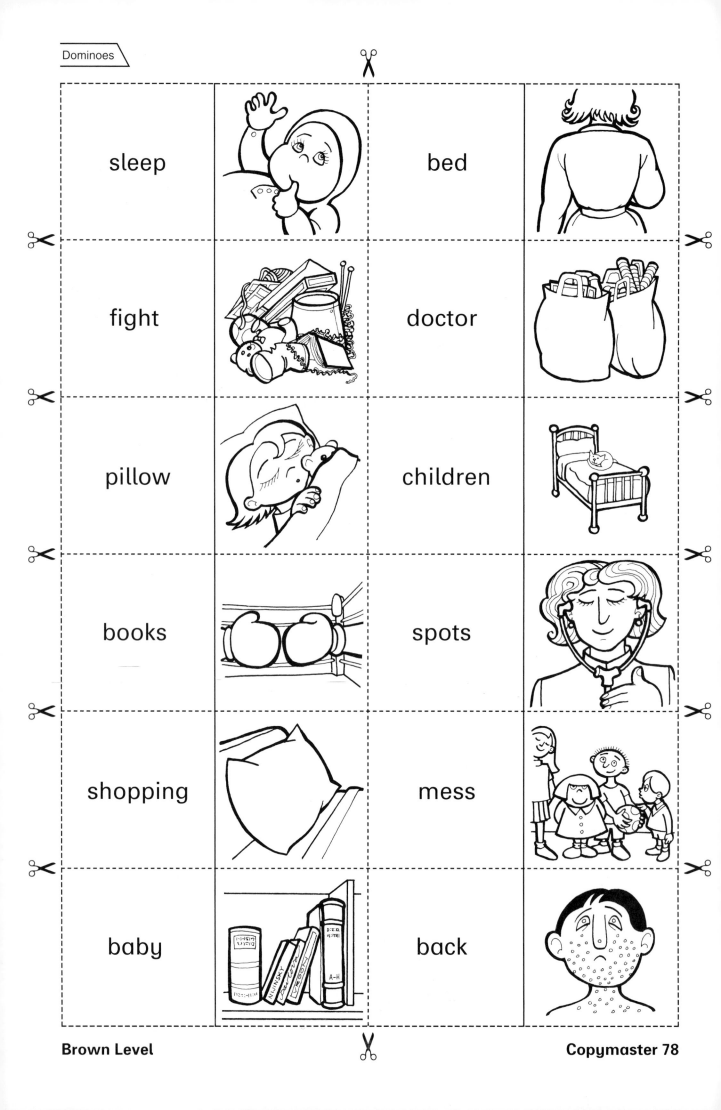

sleep		bed	
fight		doctor	
pillow		children	
books		spots	
shopping		mess	
baby		back	

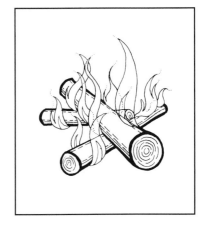

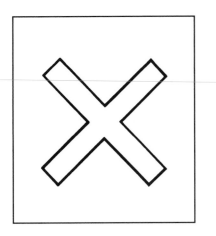

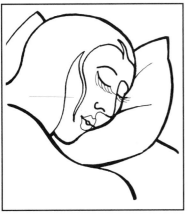

woof!

Brown Level

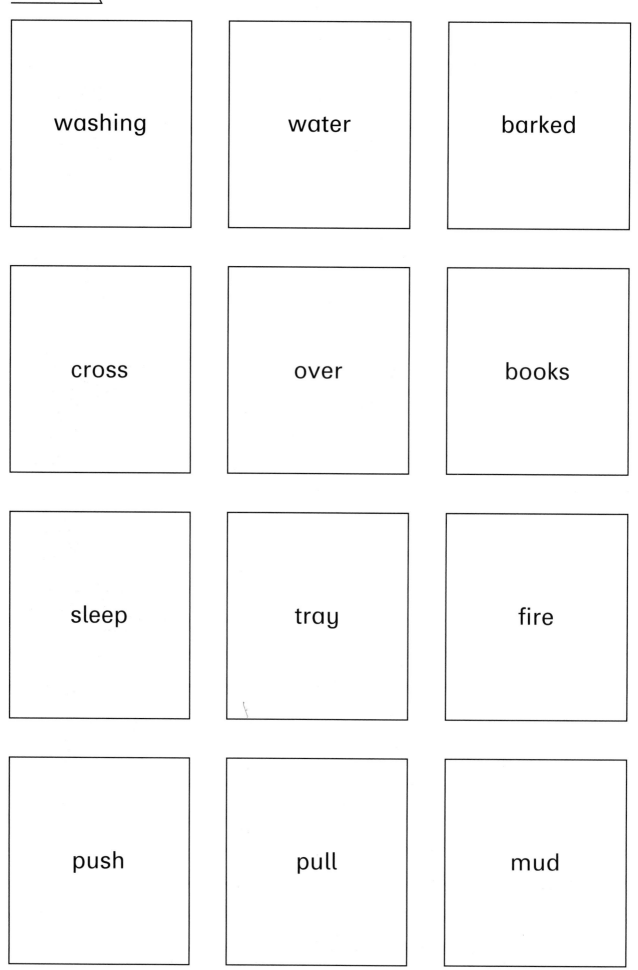

washing

water

barked

cross

over

books

sleep

tray

fire

push

pull

mud

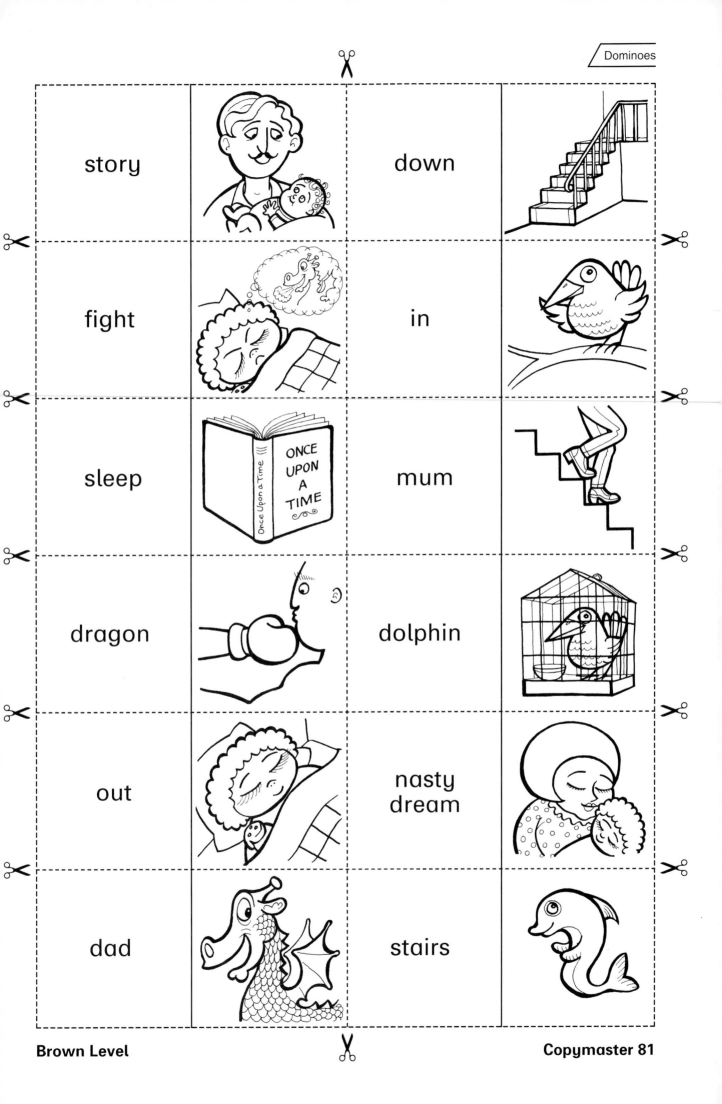

story		down	
fight		in	
sleep		mum	
dragon		dolphin	
out		nasty dream	
dad		stairs	

sleep

dragon

fight

in

out

nasty dream

story

down

stairs

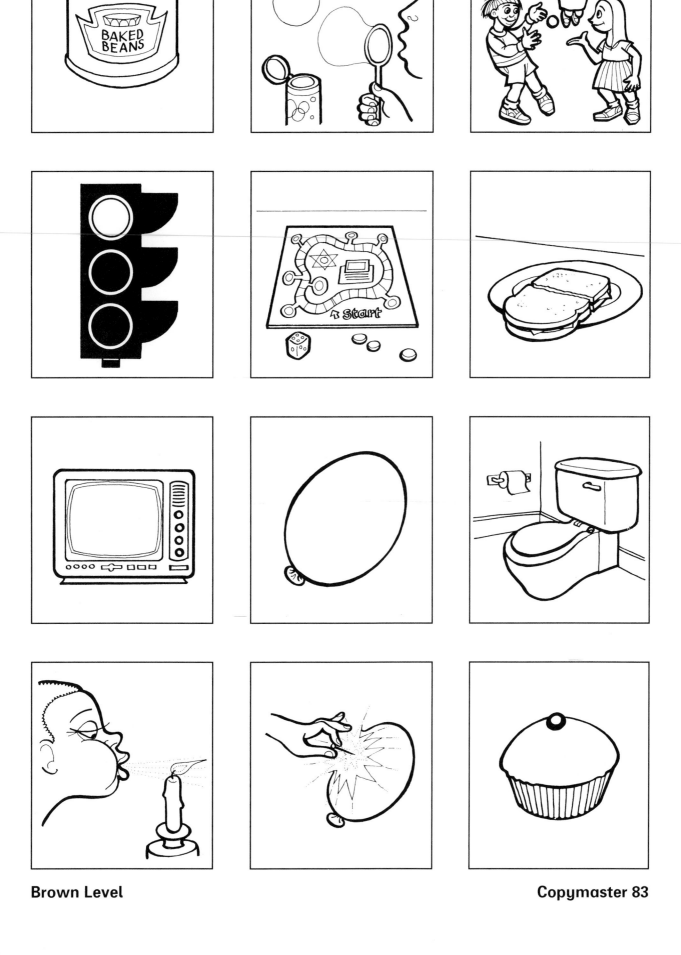

Brown Level

baked
beans

bubbles

play

stop

game

sandwich

television

balloon

toilet

blew

bang

cake

toys		tomato sauce	
cornflakes		sugar	
party		baked beans	
balloon		jam	
in		tomato	
cake		milk	

statue

shopping

balloon

bang

toilet

blew

supermarket

down

dad

balloon		down	
dad		red	blue
shopping		blew	
toilet		super-market	red
blue		mum	
bang		statue	

Brown Level

television		game	
party		cake	
birthday		stop	
bubbles		up	
everyone		play	
sandwich		mess	

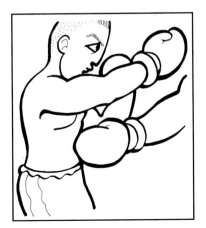  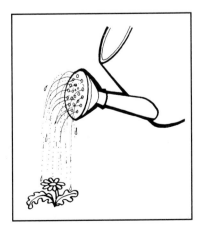

Brown Level

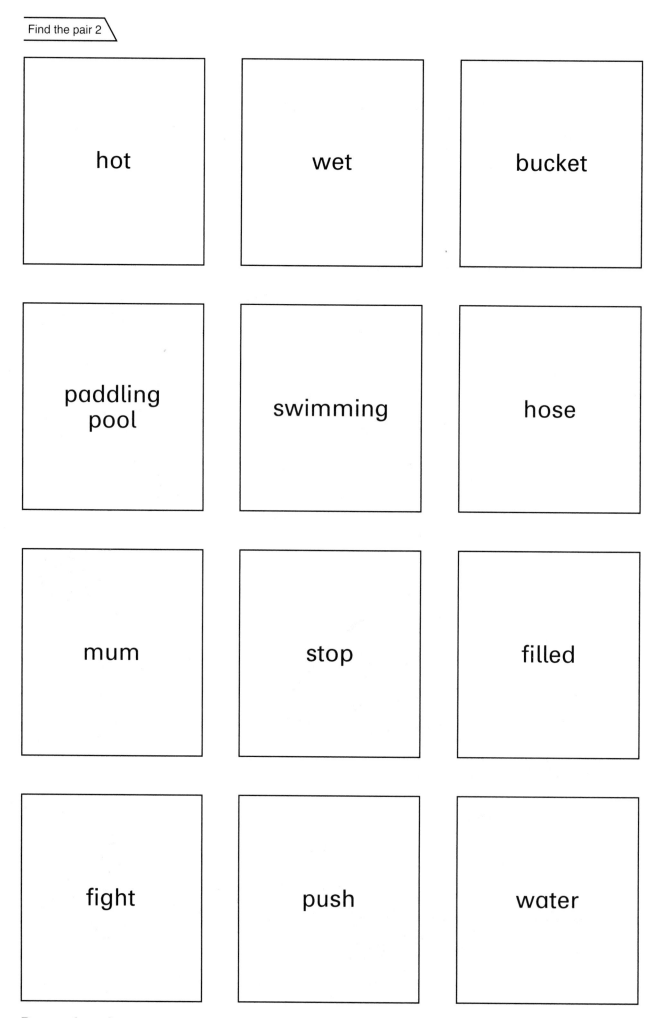

hot

wet

bucket

paddling pool

swimming

hose

mum

stop

filled

fight

push

water

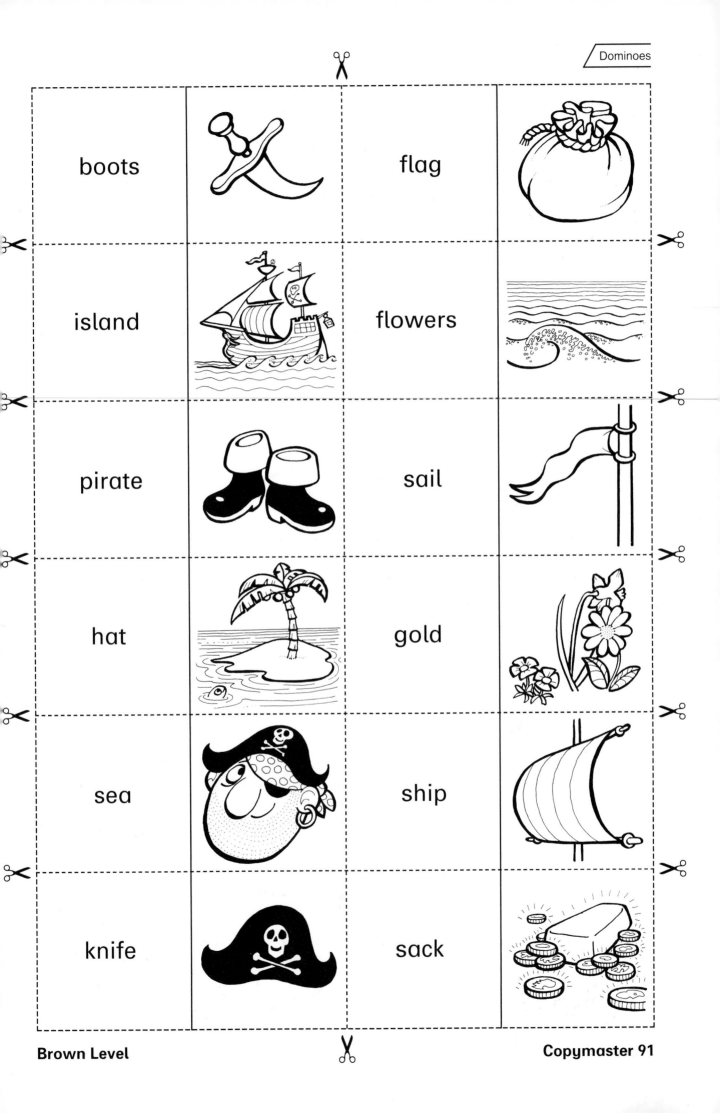

boots	*(sword)*	flag	*(sack)*
island	*(ship)*	flowers	*(sea/waves)*
pirate	*(boots)*	sail	*(flag)*
hat	*(island)*	gold	*(flowers)*
sea	*(pirate)*	ship	*(sail)*
knife	*(hat)*	sack	*(gold)*

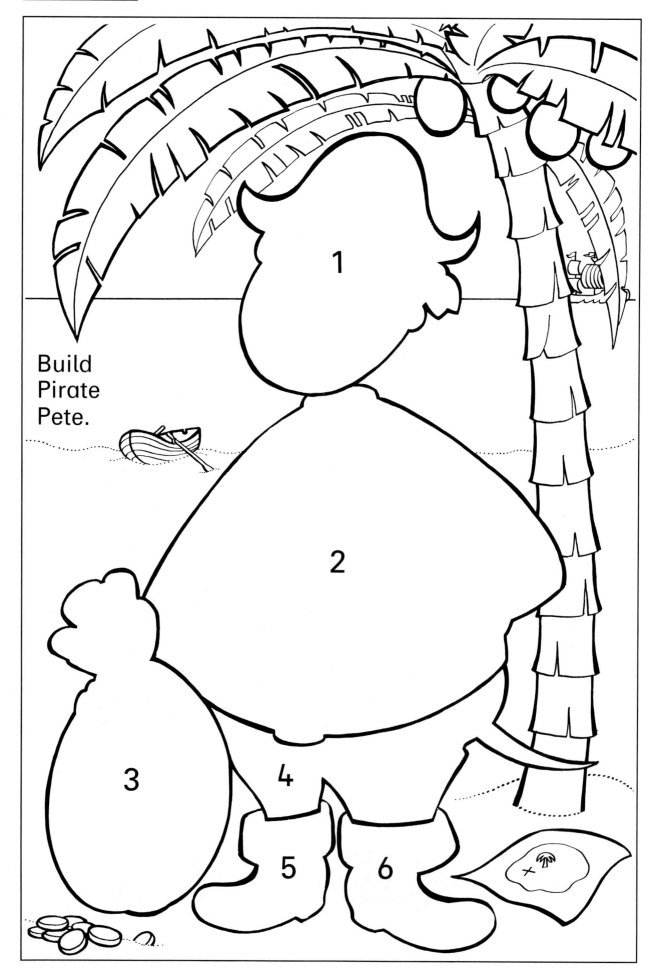

Build
Pirate
Pete.

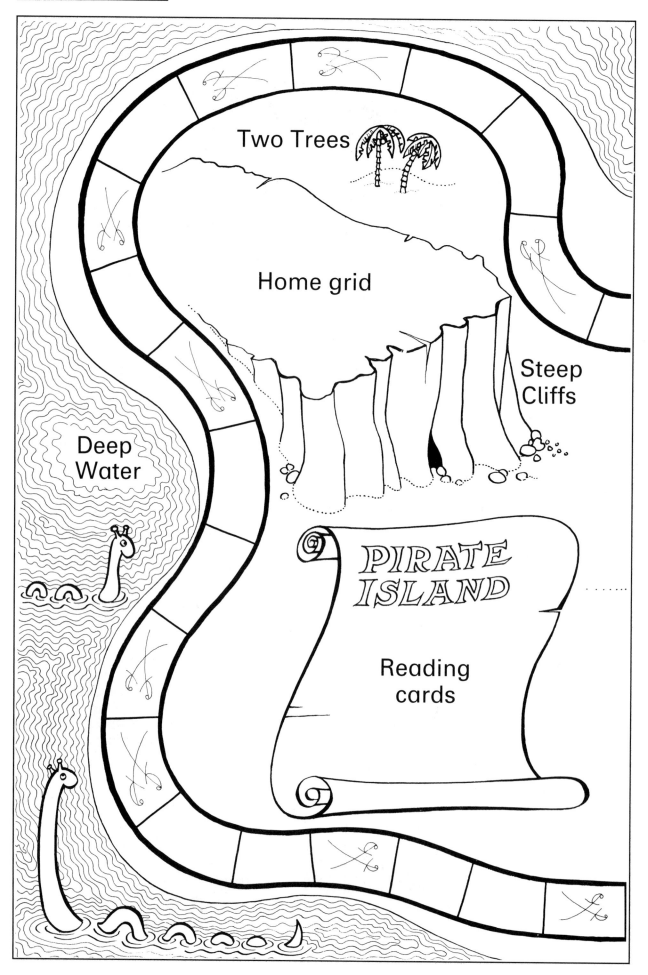

Two Trees

Home grid

Steep Cliffs

Deep Water

PIRATE ISLAND

Reading cards

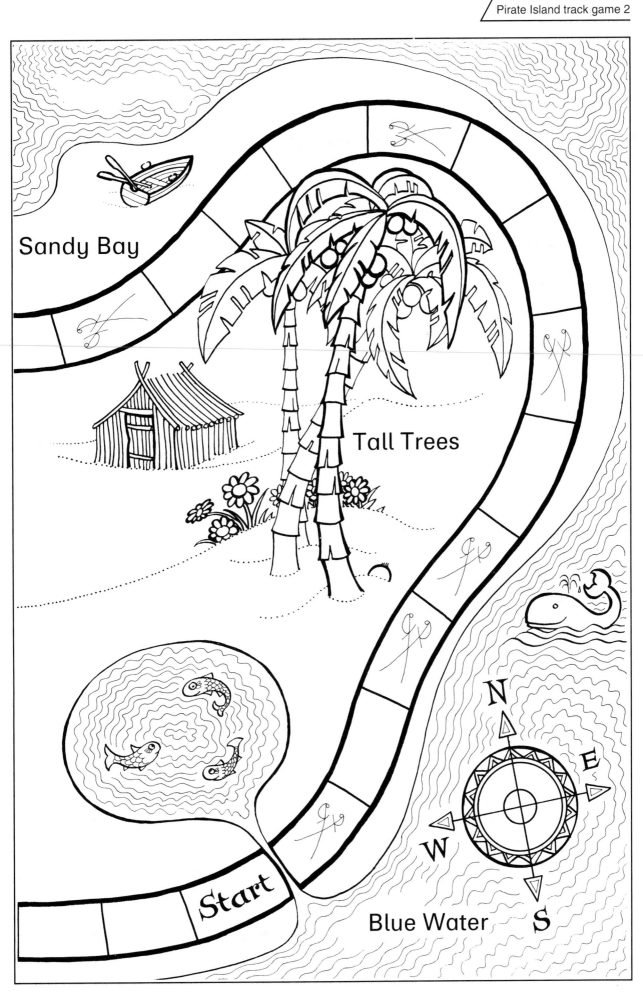

Sandy Bay

Tall Trees

Start

Blue Water

N
E
W
S

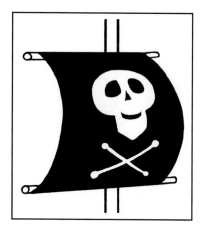

Brown Level

pirate	boots	knife
hat	island	ship
sail	flag	sack
gold	flowers	tree

blue	green	under	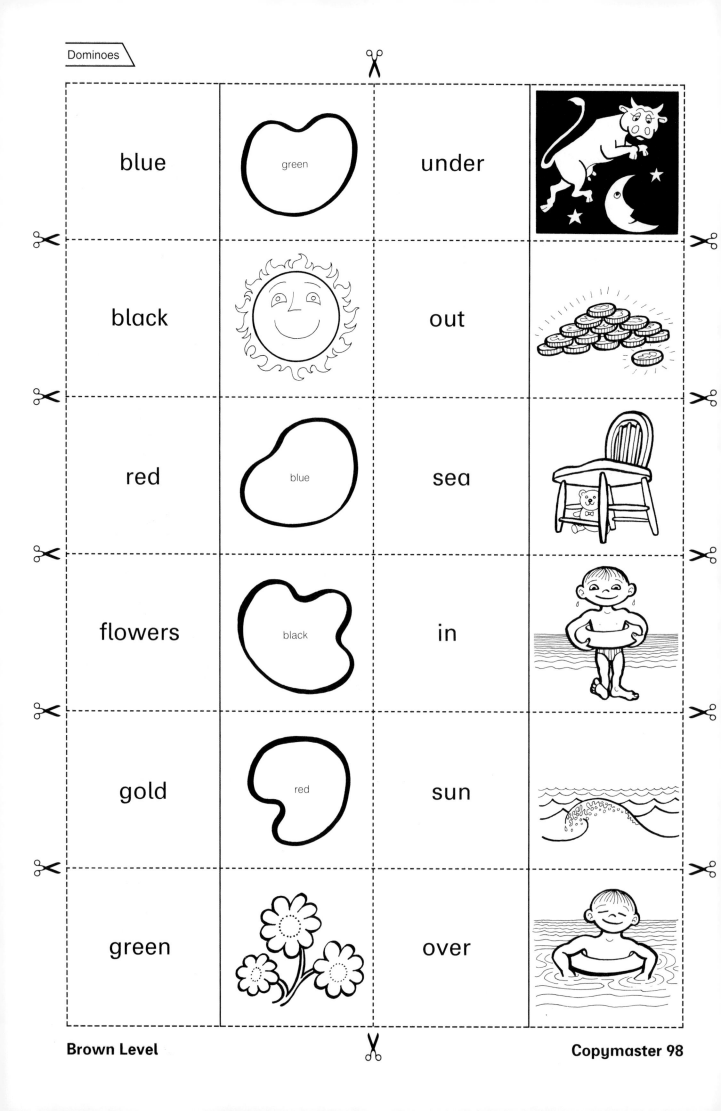
black		out	
red	blue	sea	
flowers	black	in	
gold	red	sun	
green		over	

Brown Level

pirate	witch	tree
griffin	merpeople	dragon
fire	cave	stone
seahorse	waves	sun

Match the words.

each
here
hid
under
shone
sailed
across
forgot

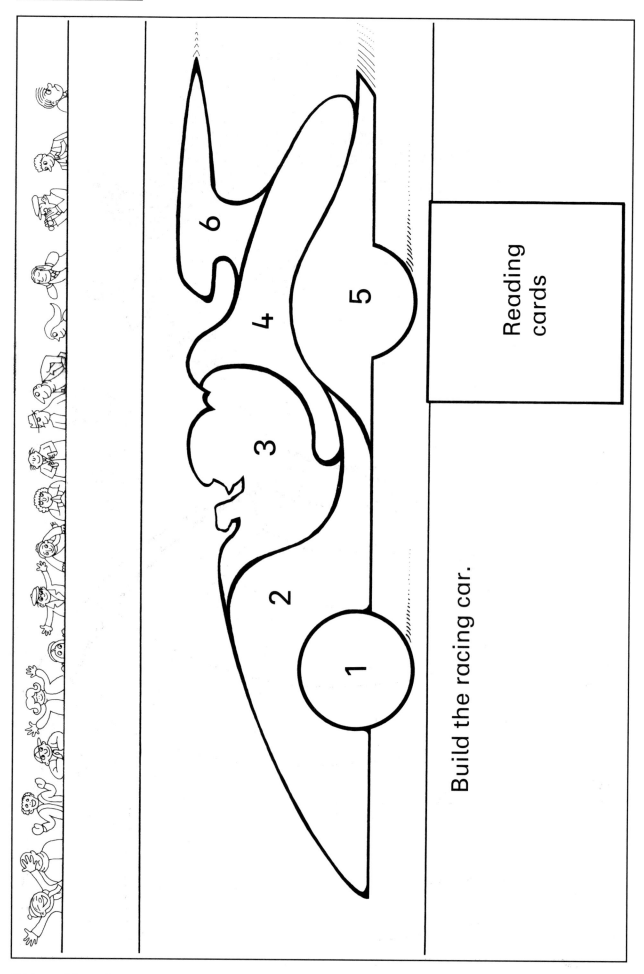

Build the racing car.

Reading cards

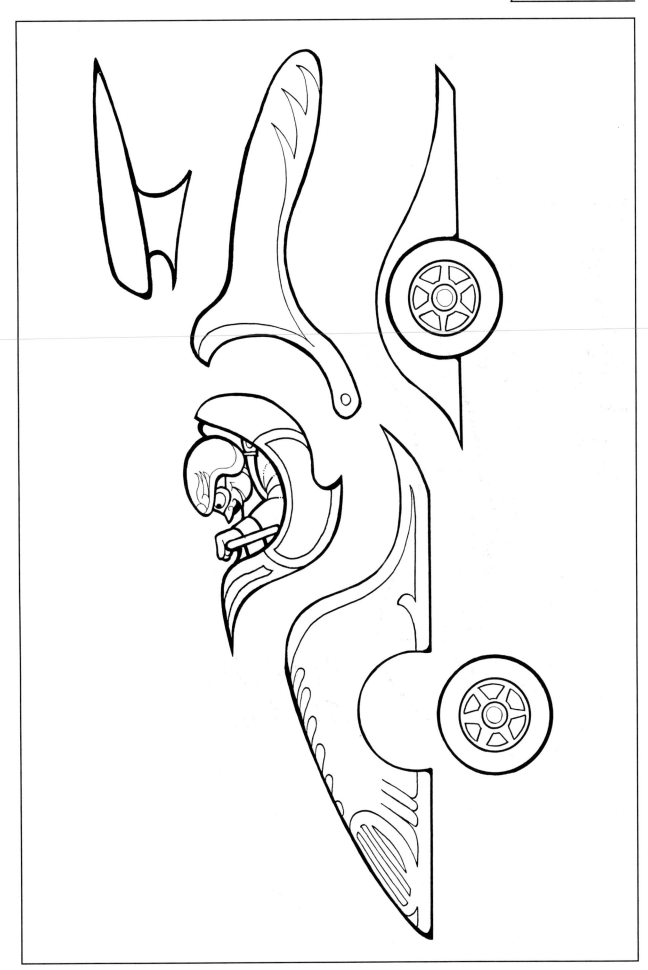

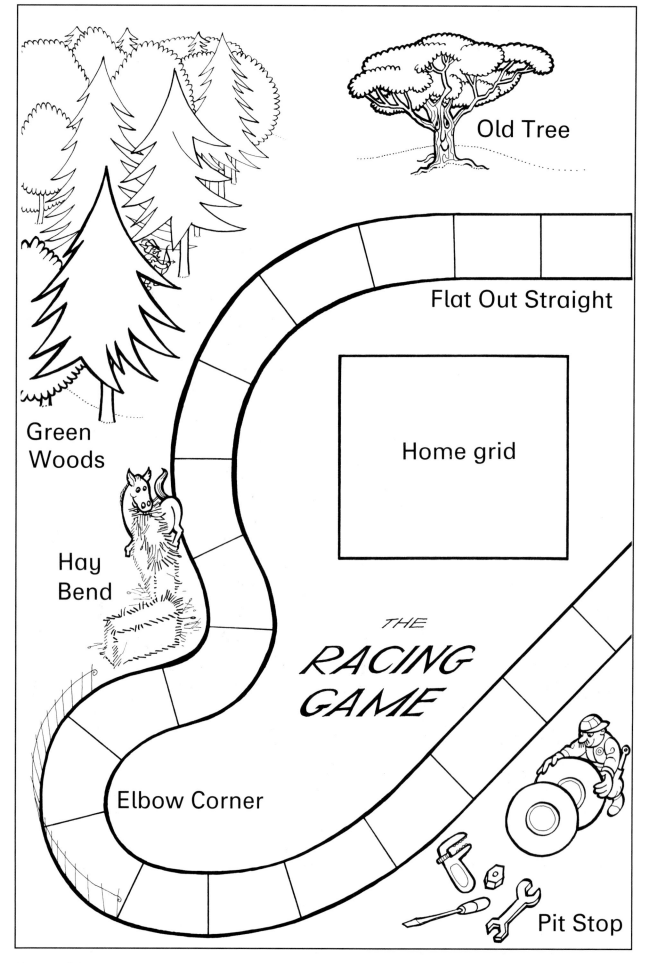

Old Tree

Flat Out Straight

Green
Woods

Home grid

Hay
Bend

THE

RACING
GAME

Elbow Corner

Pit Stop

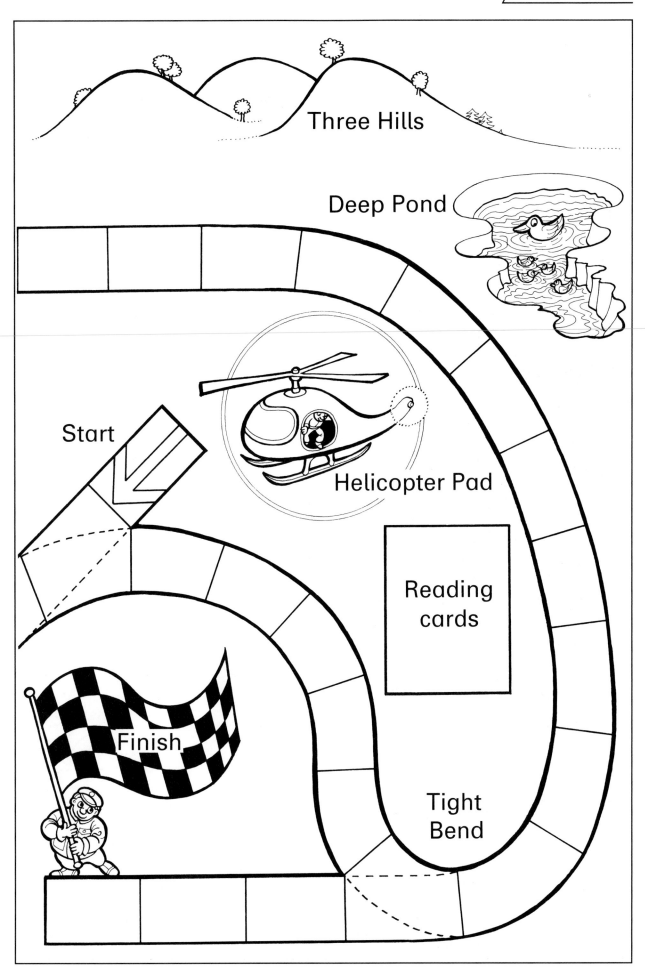

Three Hills

Deep Pond

Start

Helicopter Pad

Reading cards

Finish

Tight Bend

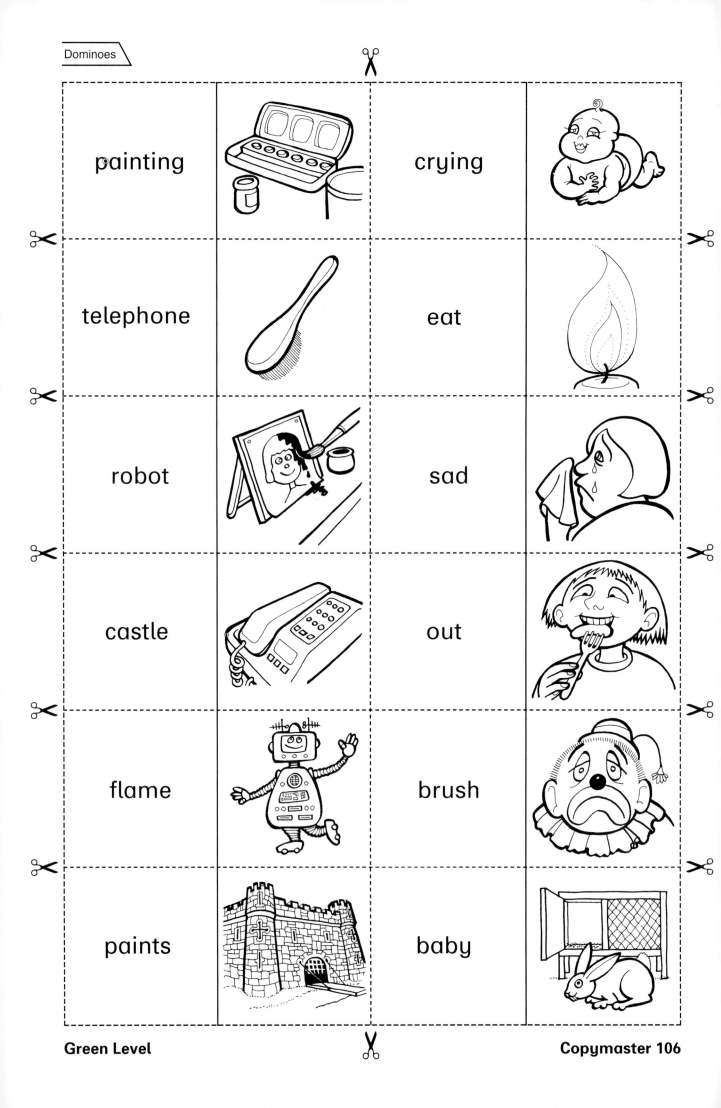

painting		crying	
telephone		eat	
robot		sad	
castle		out	
flame		brush	
paints		baby	

 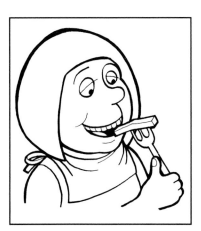 

Green Level

robot

painting

paints

castle

telephone

brush

sad

cry

baby

out

eat

flame

broom-stick	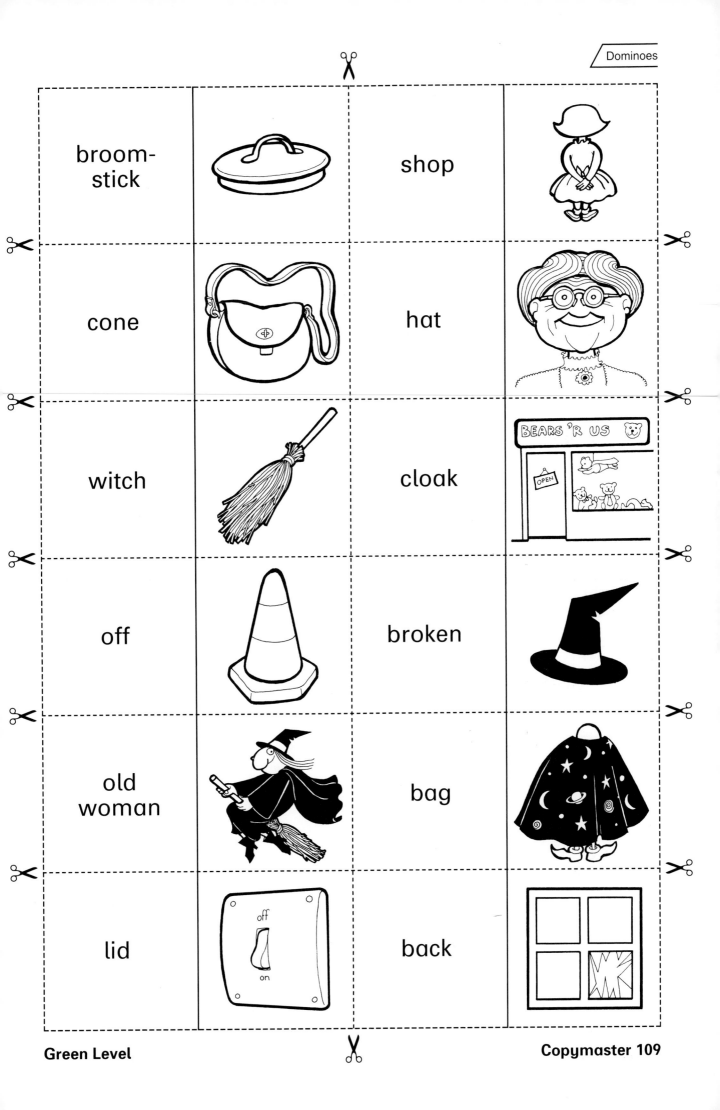	shop	
cone		hat	
witch		cloak	
off		broken	
old woman		bag	
lid		back	

boy

kick

books

pram

fire

roof

mummy

daddy

smoke

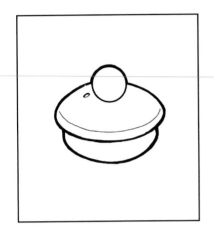
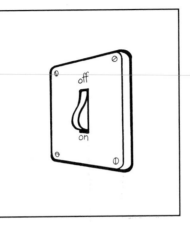
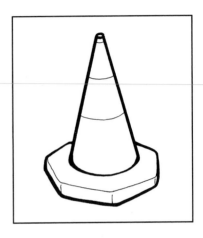

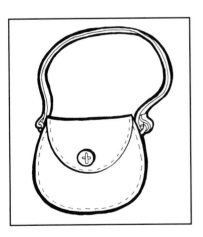

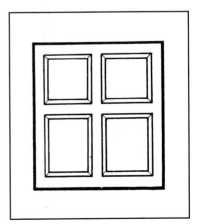

Green Level

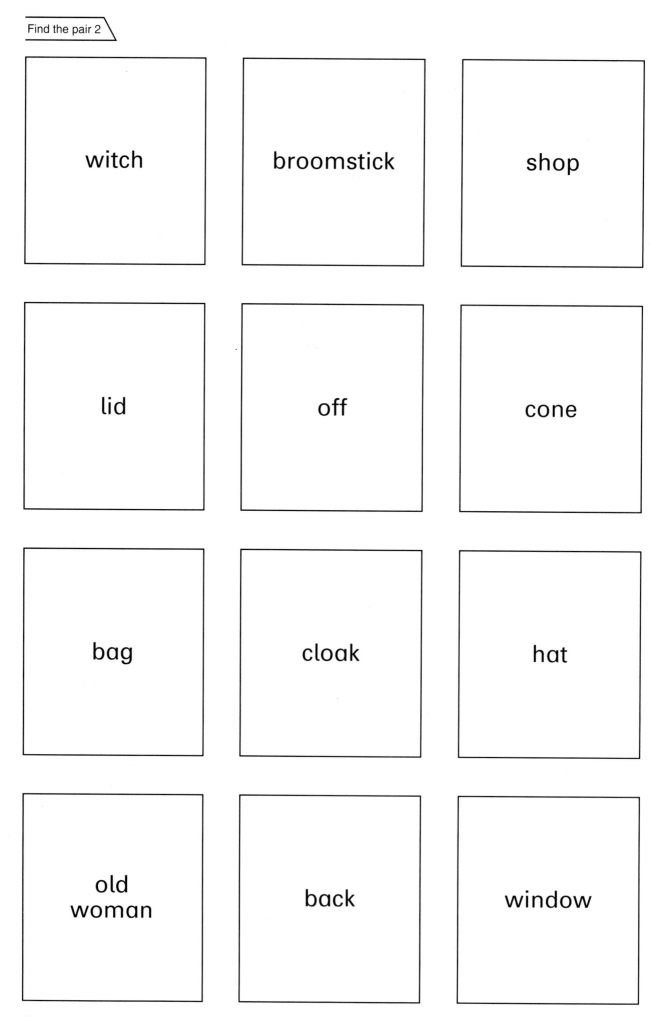

witch

broomstick

shop

lid

off

cone

bag

cloak

hat

old
woman

back

window

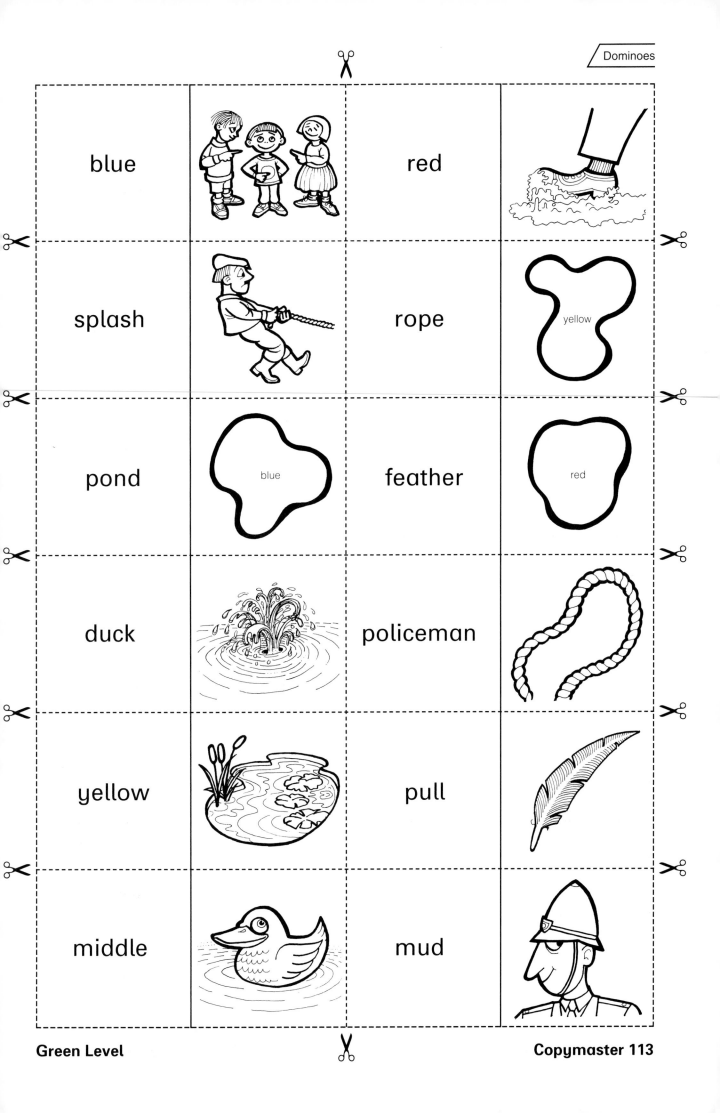

feather

pond

duck

blue

policeman

splash

rope

stick

pull

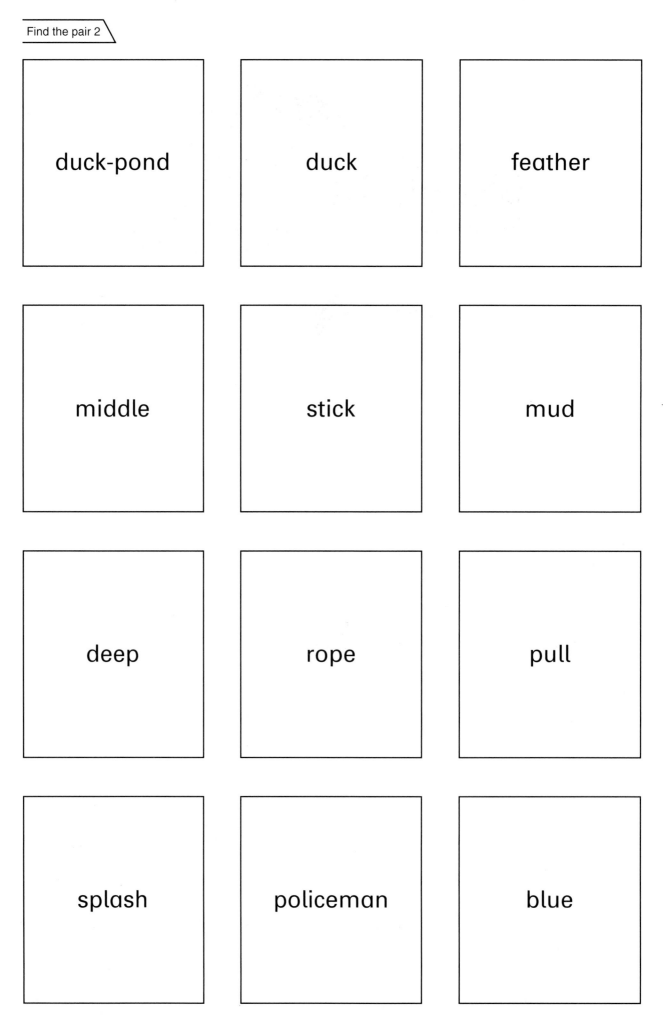

duck-pond	duck	feather
middle	stick	mud
deep	rope	pull
splash	policeman	blue

tall

from

took

they

down

an

into

He

Match the words.

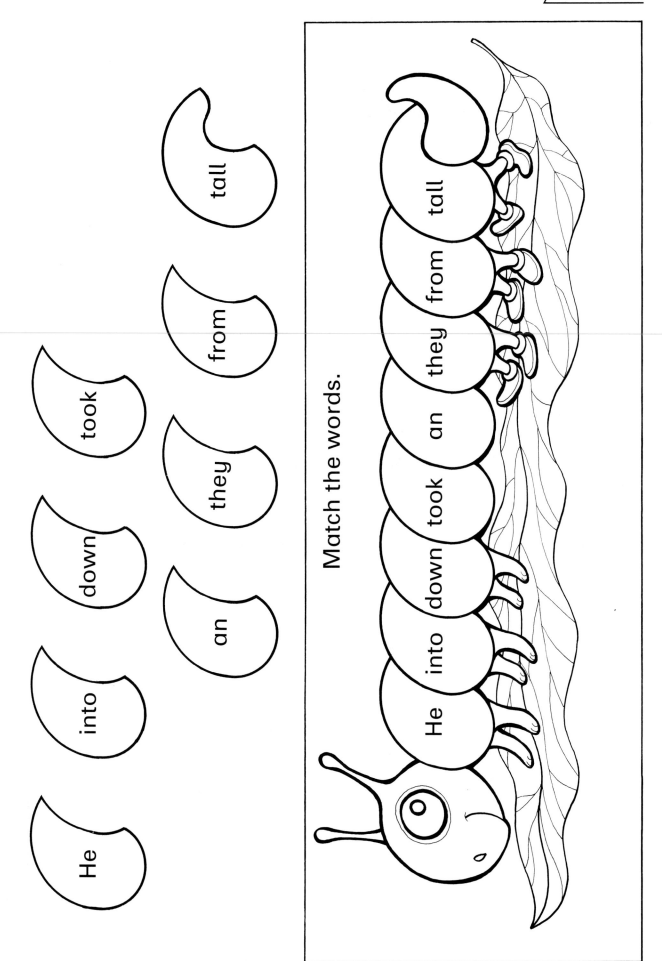

Green Level

boy		fire	
road		baby bear	
books		smoke	
one		Mummy bear	
roof		pram	
kick		Daddy bear	

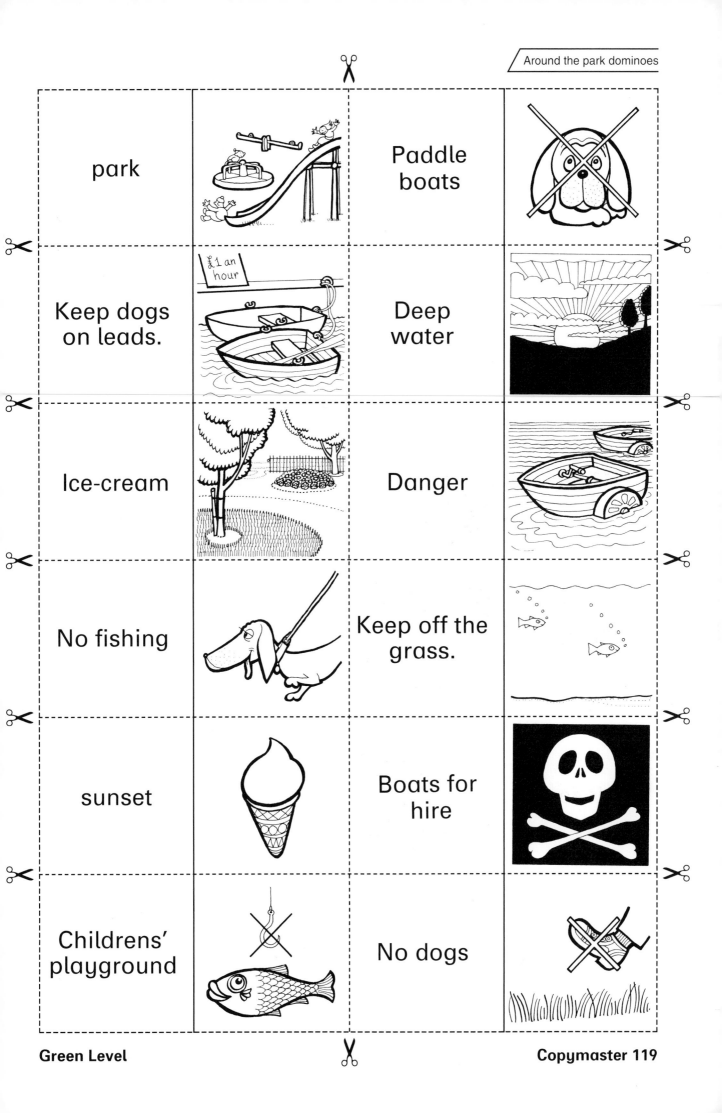

park		Paddle boats	
Keep dogs on leads.	₤1 an hour	Deep water	
Ice-cream		Danger	
No fishing		Keep off the grass.	
sunset		Boats for hire	
Childrens' playground		No dogs	

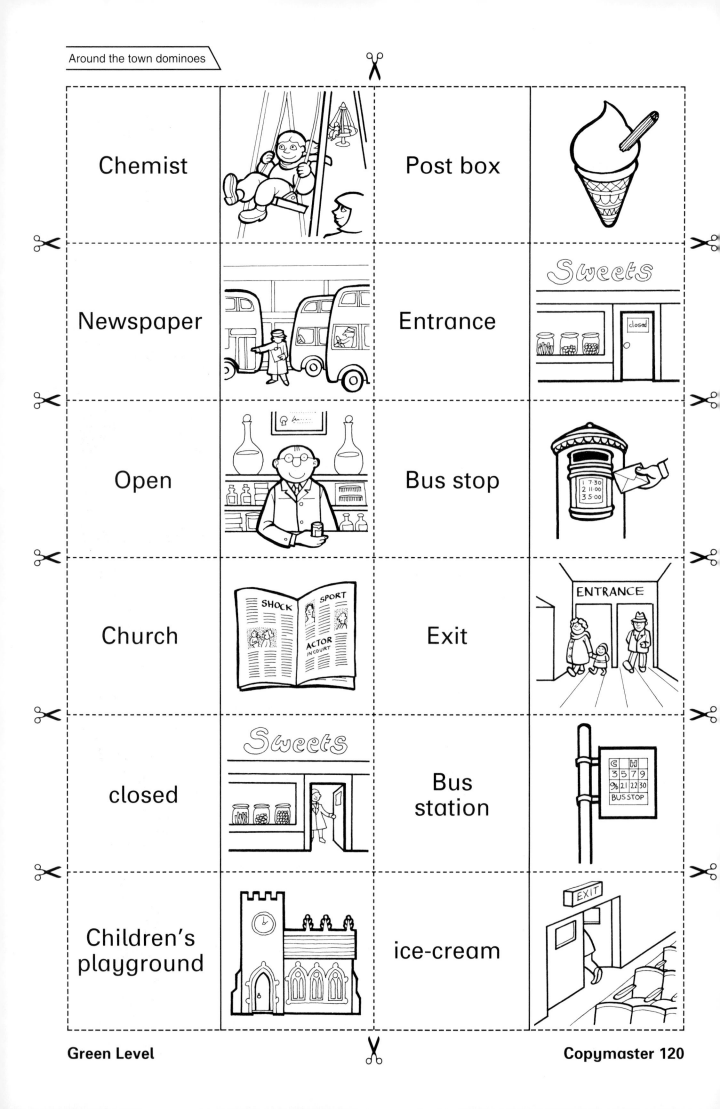

Chemist		Post box	
Newspaper		Entrance	
Open		Bus stop	
Church		Exit	
closed		Bus station	
Children's playground		ice-cream	

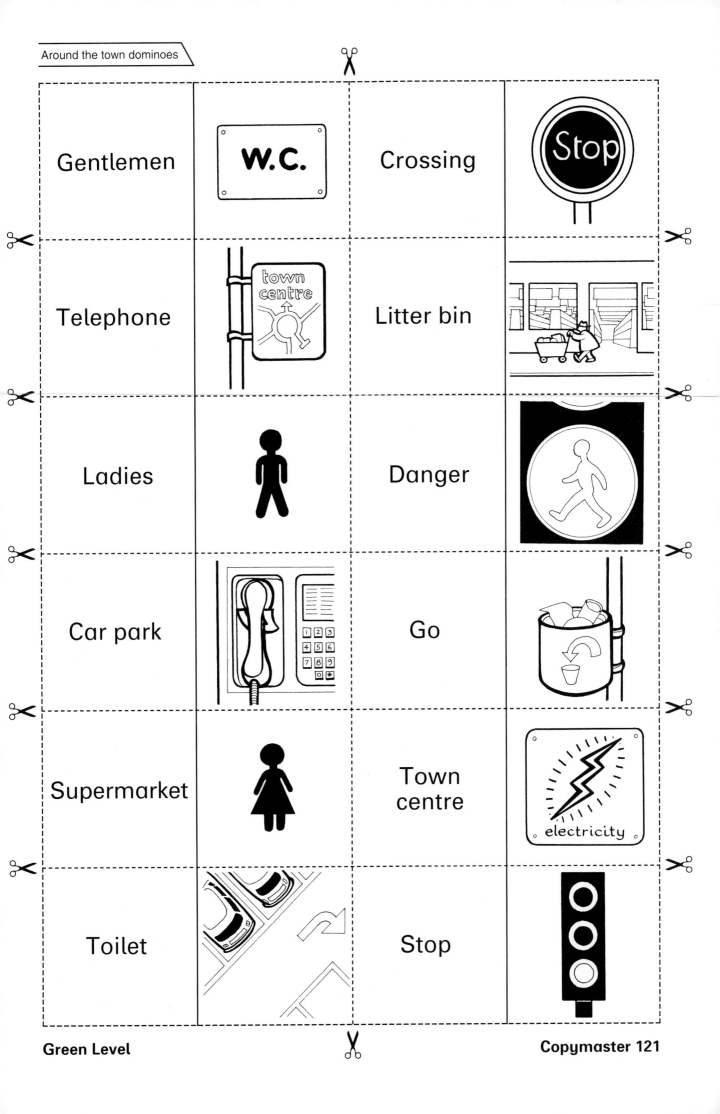

Gentlemen	W.C.	Crossing	Stop
Telephone	town centre	Litter bin	
Ladies		Danger	
Car park		Go	
Supermarket		Town centre	electricity
Toilet		Stop	

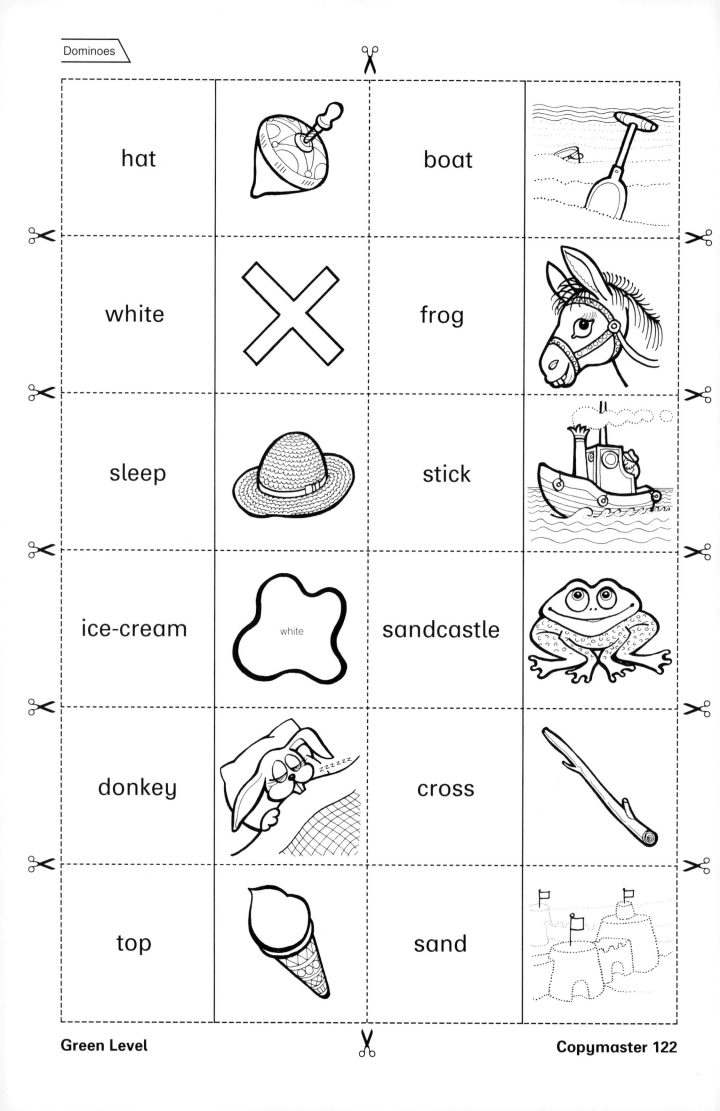

hat		boat	
white	✕	frog	
sleep		stick	
ice-cream	white	sandcastle	
donkey	zzzzz	cross	
top		sand	

asleep

sand

boat

sandcastle

frog

top

ice-cream

donkey

cross

ladder	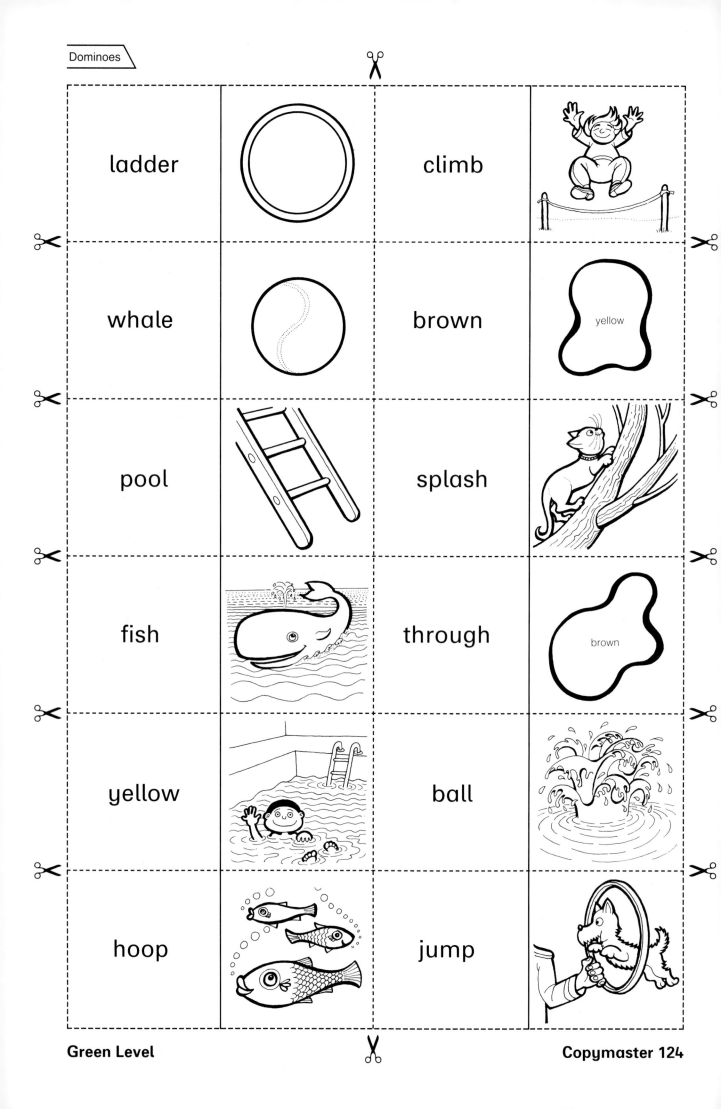	climb	
whale		brown	yellow
pool		splash	
fish		through	brown
yellow		ball	
hoop		jump	

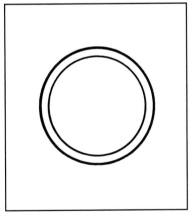

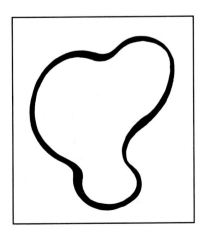
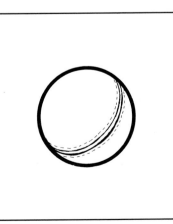
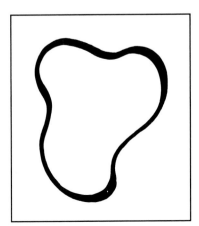

Green Level

Copymaster 125

whale	ladder	climb
splash	fish	pool
through	hoop	jump
brown	ball	yellow

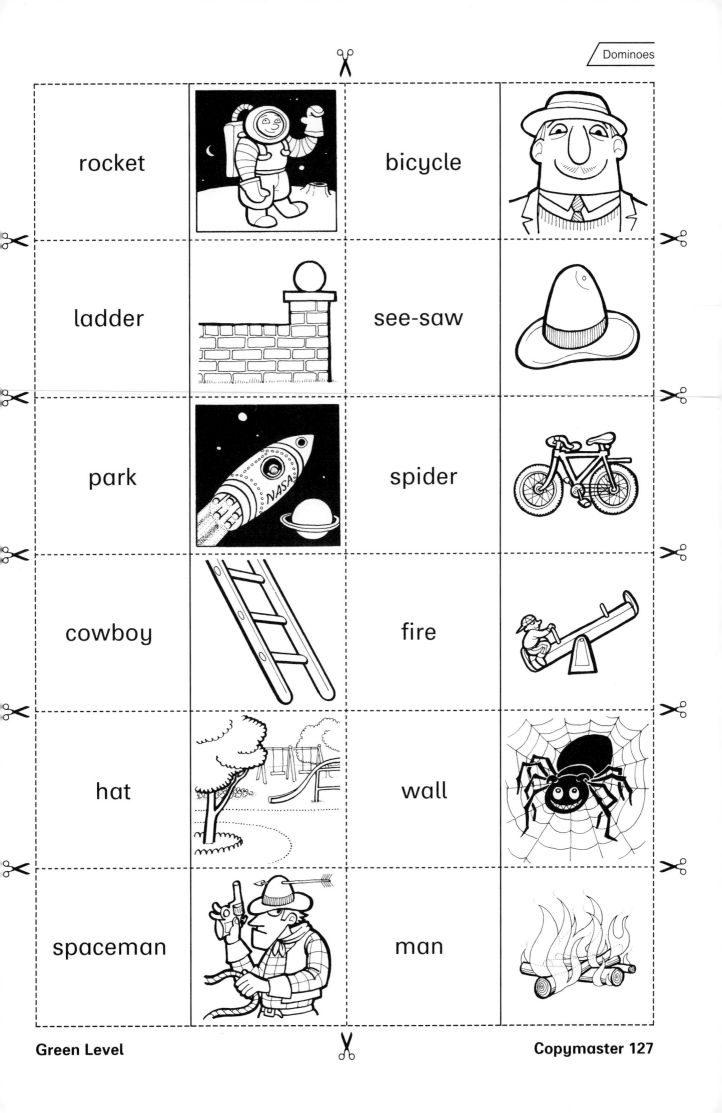

rocket		bicycle
ladder		see-saw
park		spider
cowboy		fire
hat		wall
spaceman		man

tree

teddy

bridge

shoe

car

trailer

giant

broken

sticks

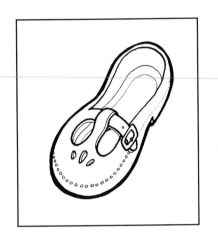

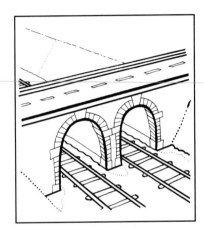

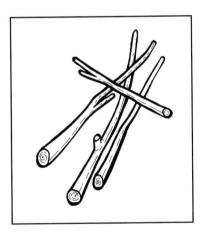
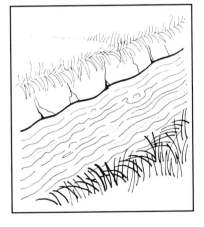

Green Level

giant	tree	teddy
shoe	trailer	bridge
sticks	stream	broken
water	man	car

rabbit		horse	
school		hop	
dog		back	
morning		one	
off		jet	
garden		milkman	1

dog

morning

back

hop

horse

school

jet

garden

rabbit

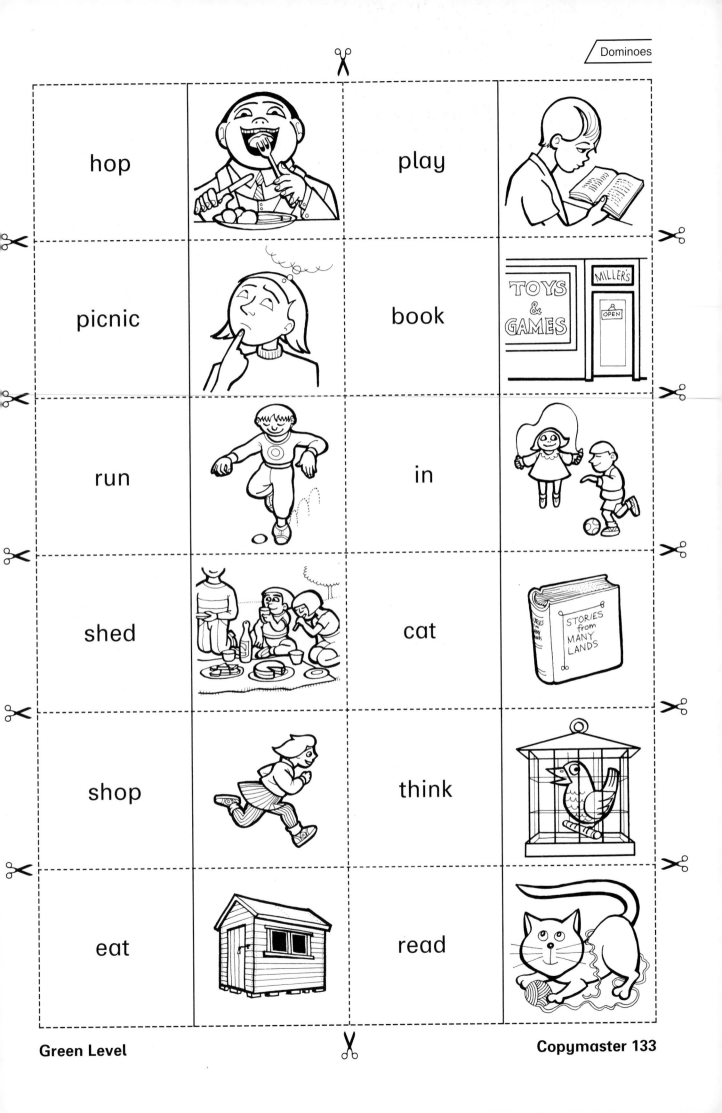

hop		play	
picnic		book	
run		in	
shed		cat	
shop		think	
eat		read	

wallpaper

key

storm

egg

witch

class

television

chimney

chair

woods	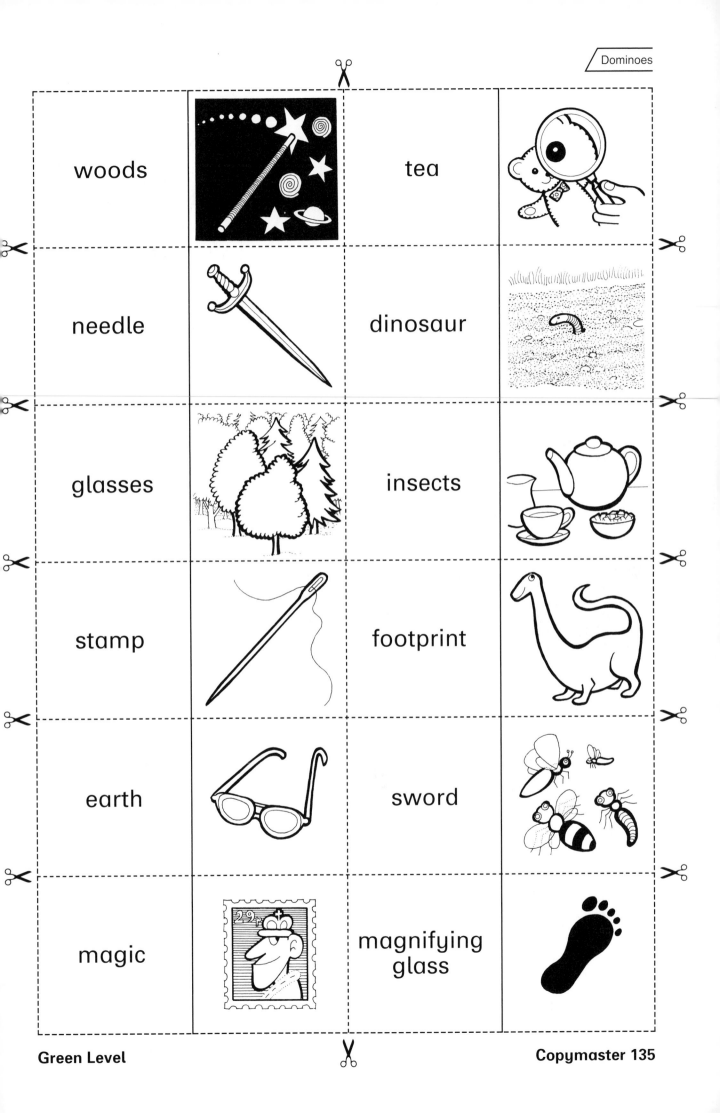	tea	
needle		dinosaur	
glasses		insects	
stamp		footprint	
earth		sword	
magic		magnifying glass	

pounds

cheese

watch

world

boots

snowballs

trousers

footprint

coat

ticket		telephone	
smile		five	
balloon		wet	
photograph		biscuits	
dream		men	
steam		key	

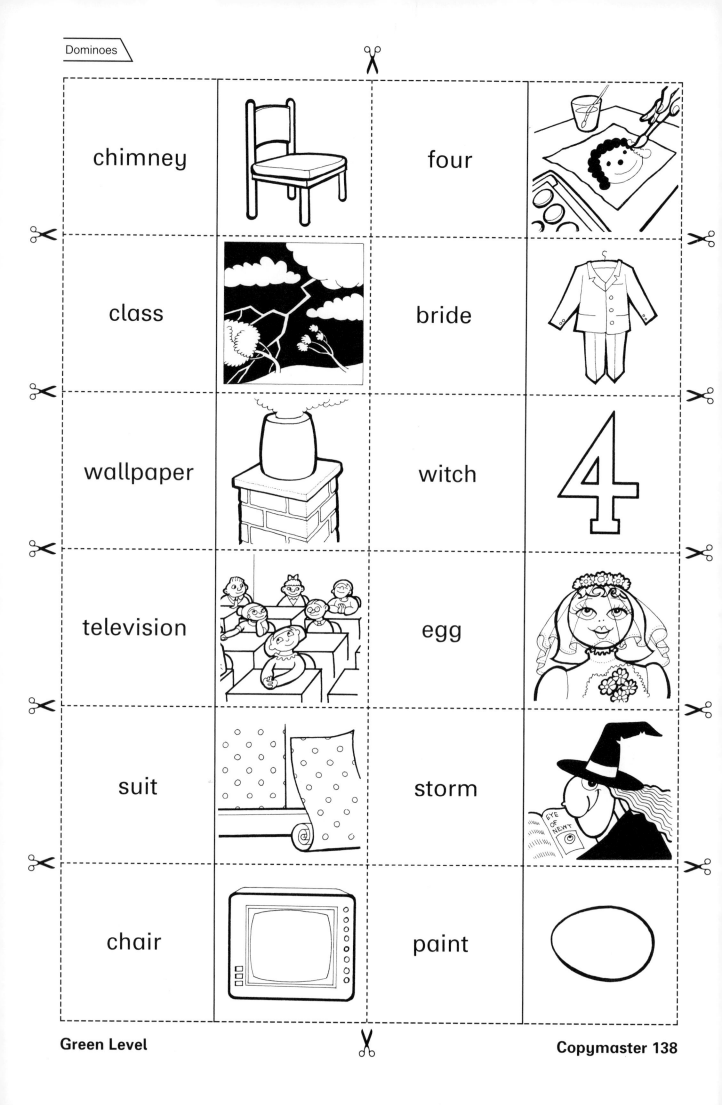

chimney		four	
class		bride	
wallpaper		witch	
television		egg	
suit		storm	
chair		paint	

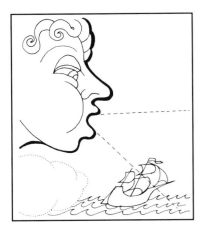

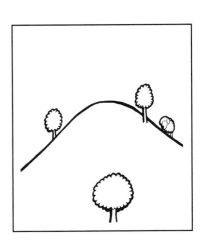

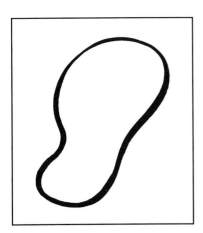

Green Level

Copymaster 139

| wind | feather | pond |
| milk | up | hill |

wind

feather

pond

road

tree

climb

milk

up

hill

white

back

down

cloth	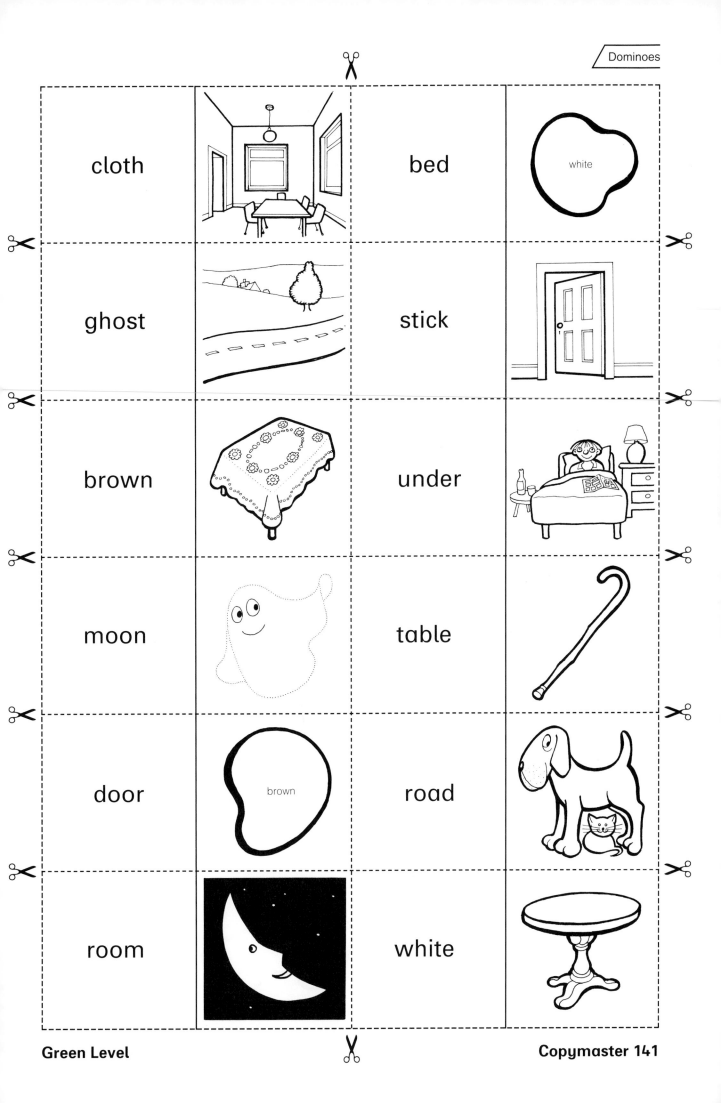	bed	
ghost		stick	
brown		under	
moon		table	
door		road	
room		white	

Green Level

Build Wordal.

Reading cards

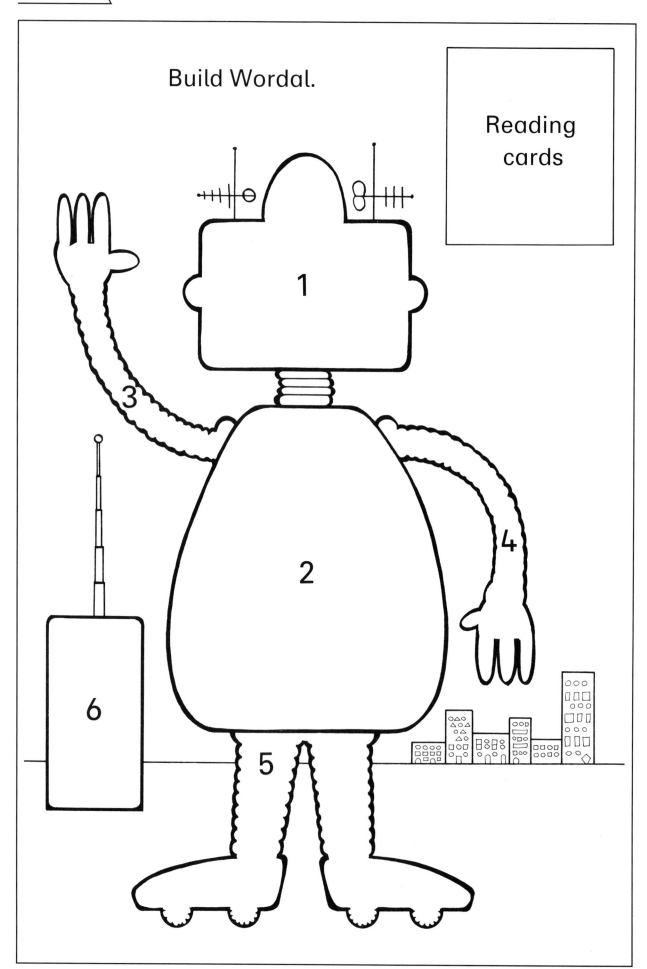

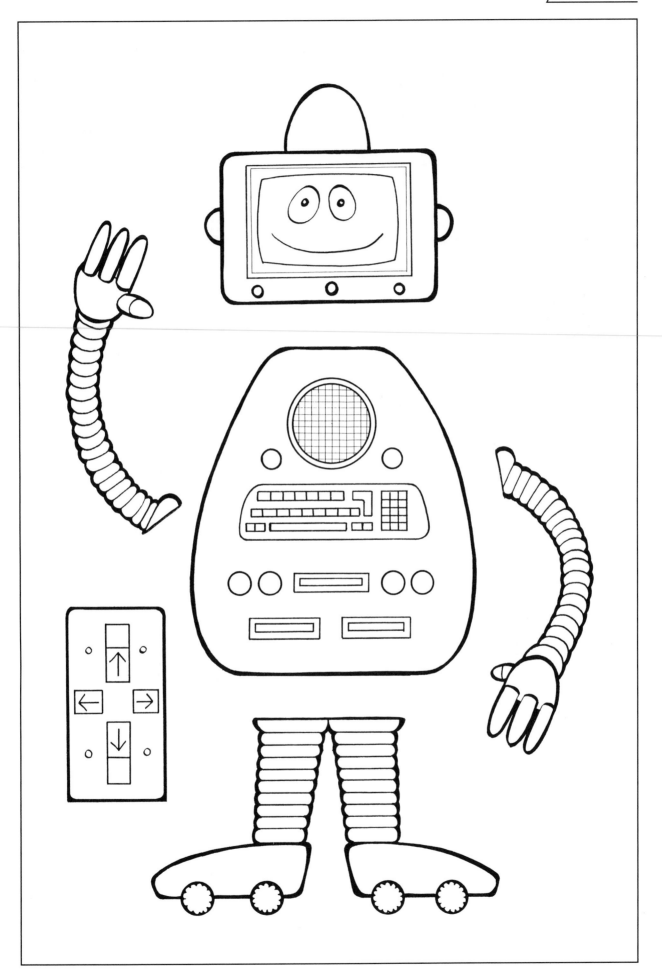

Build Asta the Alien.

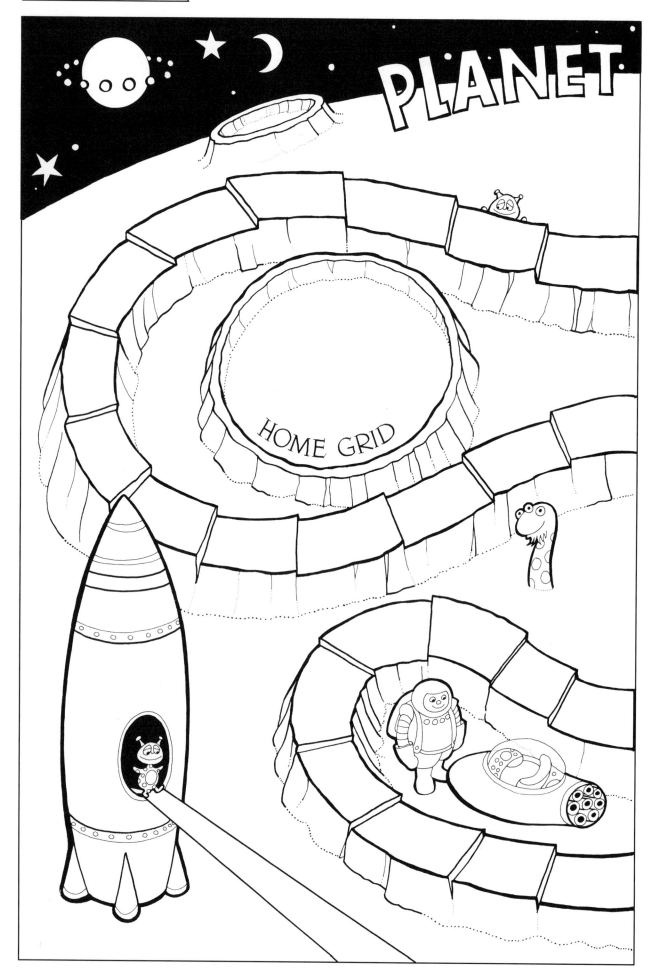

HOME GRID

PLANET

BLUEPRINTS ENGLISH RESOURCES

The **Blueprints** series provides for a very wide range of carefully structured resources for teaching English in primary schools. Alongside the core Blueprints English books for Key Stages 1 and 2, the developing Blueprints Primary English series provides more detailed coverage of essential key skills

Of particular value for use alongside the *Reading Activities Resource Bank* is *The Phonics Book*. This is a complete resource for teaching phonics in your school.

It offers clear explanations of the how and why of phonics, total coverage and a structured programme with proven classroom success. 113 child-friendly copymasters take the children through all the key sounds. Word lists, games and letters home to parents are all included, and the activities are linked to handwriting throughout. We have reproduced some sample pages below for interest.

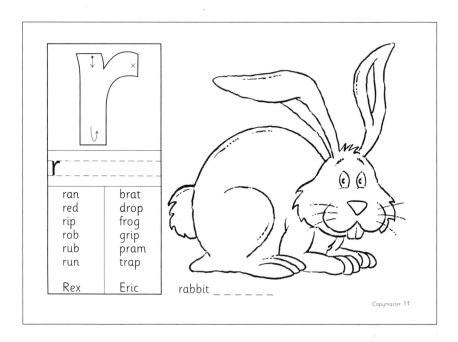

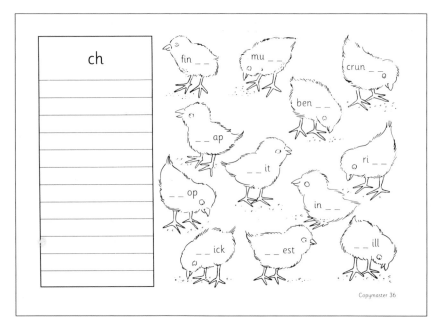